THE AUDUBON
NATURE
ENCYCLOPEDIA

THE AUDUBON
NATURE
ENCYCLOPEDIA

SPONSORED BY THE NATIONAL AUDUBON SOCIETY

VOLUME 4

EA - GO

CURTIS ⌘ BOOKS
A division of
The Curtis Publishing Company
Philadelphia — New York

CREATED AND PRODUCED BY
COPYLAB PUBLISHING COUNSEL, INC., NEW YORK

Published simultaneously in Canada by
Curtis Distributing Company, Ltd., Toronto.

Printed in the United States of America

PICTORIAL ACKNOWLEDGEMENTS, Volume 4

Hugh Spencer*, VIII, 655 bottom left, 749 middle and bottom — United States Department of Agriculture, 593 — Robert Jackowitz, 595, 659 top, 721, 714 — Allan Brooks, 597, 639, 640-41, 642-43, 646, 662, 693, 694, 778, 789, 705 — Robert Seibert, 598 top, 599, 600, 614 top — Wayne Trimm, 598 bottom, 602, 674-75, 677, 678, 679, 699, 737, 754-55, 760-61 (courtesy of New York State Conservationist) — Walter Donnen, 603 top — Samuel Grimes*, 603 bottom — Alexander Sprunt*, 604 — John Henry Dick, 606, 647 — John K. Terres, 607, 619, 644, 659 bottom — Roger Tory Peterson, 609, 638, 687, 696, 697, 733, 783, 788 — Bruce Horsfall, 611 — Allan D. Cruickshank, 612, 660, 682, 763 — W. D. Berry, 614 bottom, 633, 781 — Michael Bevans, 616, 620, 664, 776 inset — Lee Adams, 621, 645, 667, 768, 773 — Lena Scott Harris, 622, 775, 782, 784 — M. Woodbridge Williams, 623 (courtesy of National Park Service) — Sally Tate, 626-27 — Don Bleitz*, 629 — Louis Agassiz Fuertes, 632 — Clara May Hawkins, 634-35 — Charles Mohr*, 655 top right, 753 — Herbert Fennell, 665 — John H. Gerard*, 655 top left, 767 bottom, 723 — Hal H. Harrison*, 655 bottom right — Mary L. Wise, 666 — John James Audubon, 683, 726, 649 — Matthew Kalmenoff, 700, 703 — Edwin Way Teale, 704 — Harold E. Edgerton*, 707 — Jeff Swinebroad, 712 — Leonard Lee Rue III*, 724 top, — J. A. Starkey, 735, 757, 759 — George Porter*. 739 — Harold V. Green, 741, 742, 743 — Irving Kligfield, 690, 745 — Roland C. Clement, 747, 764, 765, 767 top, 650-51 — H. E. Stork*, 749 top, 752 — J. L. Sardinas, 750-51 — Donald H. Clark, 756, 758 — Richard B. Fischer, 762 — American Museum of Natural History, 771 — Bucky Reeves*, 774 — New York State Conservationist, 776 — National Park Service, 777 top — Jack E. Boucher, 777 bottom (courtesy of National Park Service) — William M. Rush*, 779 — Woodrow Goodpaster*, 792 (along with Karl H. Maslowski) — G. Ronald Austing*, 786 — Farida Wiley, 652-53, 654, 656 — Lynwood Chace*, 730 — Stephen F. Briggs*, 684 — Robert Porter Allen, 689, 691 — M. W. F. Tweedie*, 702 — Maurice Day, 708-9, 710-11 — United States Department of Labor, Soil Conservation Service, 715 — D. F. McKay, 719 (courtesy of United States Forest Service) — Dur Morton*, 724 bottom

*Photographs from Photo-Film Department of National Audubon Society

The earthworm can disappear in loose soil in two or three minutes

EARTHWORM

The common earthworm is a member of the phylum Annelida, the drawn-out, soft-bodied creatures that are composed of a variable number of segments, or rings. Leeches and many marine worms are also annelids.

Many species of earthworms occur throughout the world, wherever there is a combination of warm to moderate climate, a reliable supply of moisture in the ground, and sufficient organic debris in the soil. The animals dig their way through the earth by swallowing it, grinding it in their gizzards, and extracting anything of food value in the intestines. The wastes are usually deposited above ground, as earthen pellets called *castings.* The burrows of earthworms permit air and water to enter the soil, and the excreted castings help to enrich it.

The skin of the earthworm is a leathery cuticle, secreted by the cells that lie just beneath it, and through which the animal breathes. If it dries, it hardens, and the worm dies.

The snout is at the front end of the body, with the mouth just below it. Each segment of the body after the first has four pairs of retractable bristles, or *setae,* that are used in the animal's locomotion or progression over or under the ground. An enlarged portion of the body, at about the 32nd segment and extending back for 5 more segments, is called the *clitellum;* it produces most of the mucus that is used by the earthworm to make the cocoon for the fertilized eggs.

Each earthworm has both male and female glands. In mating, sperm cells are exchanged at the same time, then the mucus is worked forward over the head, picking up both eggs and sperm cells as it travels. Young earthworms hatch, feed on food particles within the cocoon, then break out of it to wriggle away.

In North America earthworms may reach 14 inches. Giant earthworms in Australia have been found measuring seven feet.

The value of earthworms to some birds —especially to robins and to the woodcock, which makes about half of its diet earthworms—is quite high. Earthworms have been found in stomachs of 44 species of birds by animal food-habits investigators. Earthworms are also eaten by fishes, toads, frogs, snakes, turtles, and by various mammals—shrews, skunks, and the armadillo, but especially by several species of moles.   —G.B.S.

EARWIG

Small to moderate sized insects, earwigs are nocturnal scavengers and cannibals that seek refuge in moist, shady places under stones, boards, tree bark, and piles of refuse. They also seek out the hollow stems of plants, cracks in the soil, and almost anywhere away from light. Earwigs appear to feed mainly on dead or decaying vegetable matter, but frequently eat living plants. They

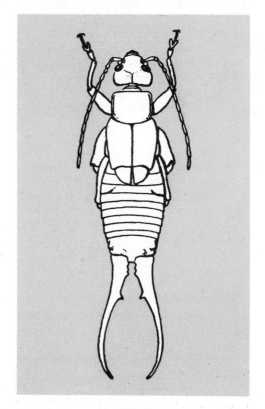

Earwig

eat many kinds of insect larvae, especially maggots, as well as their own dead. Earwigs do not crawl into human ears, as was claimed in the old tales that gave them their name.

The most striking feature of the flat-bodied earwig is the large pair of pincers, or the cerci, which grow from the last body segment. These are used defensively, chiefly to threaten, although they may be used offensively at times. Earwigs are not poisonous; however, some species produce an evil-smelling liquid that they squirt at attackers.

Earwigs belong to the small order Dermaptera, and are closely related to the grasshoppers and the termites. There are about 20 species of earwigs in North America north of Mexico. Most of them, but not all, have wings—the first pair short and leathery, the second large, membranous, rounded, and carried folded fanwise under the first. The males differ from the females in having forceps that are larger and curiously formed.

The female earwig digs a burrow for her nest and guards the eggs and the hatchlings. The young pass through from four to six molts to become full-grown at slightly more than half an inch long. Tropical species are larger and more colorful.

Generally, earwigs are harmless, but they can become garden pests. They attack flowers such as roses and dahlias by cutting the petals off at the base.
—G.B.S.

ECHINODERM

The name echinoderm means spiny skin, and it has been given to a phylum of marine invertebrates, the Echinodermata. Included in this group are the sea lilies, the starfishes, the brittle stars, the sea urchins, and the sea cucumbers.

Most members of the animal kingdom are bilaterally symmetrical. They have two practically identical sides, and most external and internal organs are paired. Echinoderms have evolved a different pattern. They are radially symmetrical

in fives, or multiples of five; from a central point, they can be divided into five nearly identical pieces, as one would slice a pie. However, the larval stage exhibits bilateral symmetry.

Echinoderms have a distinctive method of locomotion. The tube feet, which usually have suckers on the end, are operated by water pressure. Each foot is controlled by a sac, called an *ampulla;* when it is contracted, the pressure of the water inside it forces the foot outward, and when it is relaxed the foot springs back.

In most echinoderms the sexes are separate. The reproductive cells are disseminated into the water, and fertilization takes place outside the body of the animal.

Sea lilies resemble flowers, with their feathery tentacles set on a long stalk made of lime. Starfishes usually have five arms; if one is cut off, a new one is grown to replace it, and often the severed arm will grow four more to become a new individual. The brittle stars have very long, thin, delicate arms, also usually five. Sea urchins live surrounded by their own feet; the radial symmetry is apparent only after the feet have been cleared away. Sea cucumbers are cylindrical, but their symmetry is apparent when they are viewed head on.   —G.B.S.

ECOLOGY

Ecology is the study of animals and plants in relation to each other and to the physical environment of their natural habitat. The word *ecology,* first used in 1869 by Ernst Haeckel, the German zoologist, is based on a Greek word meaning *home.* To study a plant or animal *ecologically* is to observe a species in the home where it lives naturally and where it is intricately dependent on all the other plants and animals and physical features —rainfall, altitude, soil, and so on—with which any species coexists.

Ultimately, ecology is why taxonomists classify, anatomists dissect, or embryologists look through microscopes. Ecol-

A deer in its forest home

ogy is a synthesis of the life sciences, the goal of biology. It is a way of looking at the world of nature that was not possible until after biologists had learned to classify and to understand the workings of individual plants and animals.

In 1885 the Danish botanist Warming discovered that plants live in definite *communities*—that certain kinds of plants grow together if the physical environment is the same. It was not until 1909 that Warming's important book *Oecology of Plants* was translated into English. Four years later the British Ecological Society was formed. In 1916 the Ecological Society of America was founded.

Biologists everywhere began to study communities. They prowled along seashores and observed that the seaweeds —algaes and kelps—are separated in definite "bands" along the shore; some grow only at the low tide line, others where they are stranded "high and dry"

for several hours a day. They observed the honeycomb worms on exposed sea cliffs where the surf pounds against the shores and noted that the worms are found only where sand is available for building their homes and where the rocks are partially protected from the sea. On the same cliff rocks exposed to the sea's full onslaught they found mussels and barnacles attached by threads or cemented to the rocks. On the highest cliffs, where the water seldom comes, they found periwinkles crawling along rocky crevices.

Other ecologists discovered that at low altitudes in the Rocky Mountains near Denver, ponderosa pine dominates the forest. Higher up no ponderosa pine grows, but lush growths of spruce and fir thrive. Higher still, where the trees were unable to grow at all, plants cling close to the ground and are protected from the high winter winds; there they form a vast tundra community where ptarmigans scratch out nests among the lichens.

In tropical rain-forest communities, where sunlight never reaches the ground, towering trees of great variety thrust their tops out of the darkness below. Lianas, the woody vines that grow in the rain forest, twine ever upward through the trees to reach the sun. Below, nothing grows but those plants that gain their nourishment directly from the trees or the rotting litter on the forest floor.

Ecologists have only begun to understand the processes by which communities of animals and plants become established. Although there is general agreement among ecologists on large divisions—or *biomes* such as coniferous forest, tundra, or desert (*see under Life Zone*)—they disagree as to what constitutes a community in *climax*—the state of equilibrium among all plants and animals that is reached if the community is allowed to grow undisturbed without the interference of man or natural disasters such as fire. Man, however, is also part of the environment and so are natural disasters. The adaptations of plants and animals are such that floods, fires, earthquakes, landslides, and volcanic activity are taken in stride, but nature cannot always cope with the activities of man.

In a national park in the western United States a ski area was recently constructed in a blue spruce forest that had escaped fire damage for centuries. The huge trees, the moss-covered forest floor, the cathedral-like hush of the spruce stand was destroyed by the chainsaw as it steadily cut great swaths of trees where ski runs would be.

Since the opening of the recreation area, there has been little skiing on the lower slopes where the great trees stand, but the wind blowing into the forest along the ski trails has toppled, one by one, some of these great trees, whose shallow roots could no longer support them.

Inevitably, ecology is linked with conservation. It is impossible to form sound conservation policy without knowledge of the complex interrelationship between species. Slowly progress is being made. The predator-prey concept has been well worked out (*see under Bounty System and under Predation*). For example, the needless slaughter of bobcats by ranchers in eastern Colorado led to a tremendous rise in the population of cottontails and jackrabbits (*See Food Chains and also Balance of Nature*). The decimation of the golden eagle has led to an increase of rodents that are a serious threat to crops (*See Eagle: Golden Eagle*).

The study of ecology has offered insight into the question of what environmental factors are beneficial or detrimental to the survival of plants and animals. Only with this insight can the growing list of extinct species be checked. (*See also under Wildlife: Wildlife Community*)

—G.A.B.

Recommended Reading

Basic Ecology—Ralph and Mildred Buchsbaum. The Boxwood Press, Pittsburgh.
Ecology of Animals—Charles Elton. John Wiley & Sons, Inc., New York.
Fundamentals of Ecology—Eugene Odum. W. B. Saunders Company, Philadelphia.

EDGE EFFECT

Edge is a narrow area between two adjoining plant communities. The edge contains a mixture of one or more plant groups, and the effect on the numbers and kinds of animals present in the immediate vicinity is known among wildlife management experts as the "edge effect."

Students of animal populations have noticed that wildlife species of low mobility, such as bobwhite quail that may spend weeks or months on a quarter acre of land, tend to be attracted and held by habitats that include several types of vegetation—for example, field and forest—within a small area. It is found, actually, that the more distinct

Robins are numerous where vegetation is varied

the contrast between different vegetational types, the greater the population of such species as bobwhite. This is simply another way of saying that the area that provides easy access to the widest diversity of habitats will be favored by species that have many requirements or preferences as to food and cover. This is especially true if the species are not inclined to travel far to satisfy these requirements.

Many of the familiar songbirds—robins, song sparrows, etc.—are also species of low mobility, at least during the nesting season. Such birds will also be most numerous where there is a generous mixture of different vegetational types—in this case, lawn, shrubbery, neglected corners grown to weeds, and trees, both deciduous and evergreen.(*See also under Hedge*) —R.C.C.

EEL

These elongated fishes, bear a certain resemblance to snakes and are sometimes confused with the true sea snakes. However, all eels, except one tropical form, have a pair of pectoral fins and a long caudal fin, and one pair of gill slits. Most eels have no scales, although a few have tiny ones within the skin.

Eels live in both fresh and salt water. The moray eels, found along rocky and coral shores throughout the tropics, have a well-earned reputation for viciousness. Both the European eel and the American eel spawn in the Atlantic Ocean, south and east of Bermuda. The young make their way to the European and American coasts, where the males reside in the salty lagoons and bays while the females travel great distances up freshwater rivers. They live there several years before returning to the ocean to spawn and die. —G.B.S.

American Eel

Other Common Names—Common eel, freshwater eel, silver eel
Scientific Name—*Anguilla rostrata*
Family—Anguillidae (eels)
Order—Apodes
Size—Length, four to five feet
Range—Atlantic Coast, inhabiting all rivers east of the Rocky Mountains from Mexico north to Maine. Also found in the West Indies and south through Central America to Brazil

Life History of the Freshwater Eel

Off the North American continent, southeast of Bermuda and northeast of Puerto Rico, lies a tract of sluggish water known to mariners as the Sargasso Sea. There, below the weed-choked surface, is the breeding and spawning grounds of both the American and European eels.

Of all fishes known to mankind, none has puzzled scientists for so long a time as have the freshwater eels of the rivers

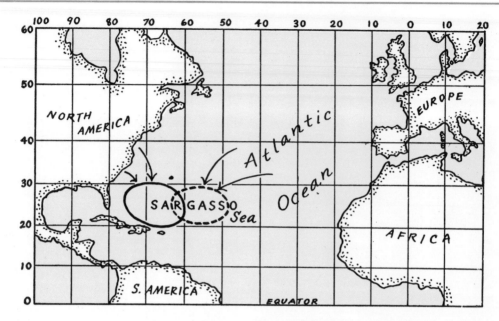

The breeding and spawning grounds of both the European and American fresh-water eels are near the Sargasso Sea

and lakes of Europe and America. Down through the centuries they have been a food delicacy in European and Mediterranean countries, but their migratory habits and methods of propagation remained unexplained. Men knew that each autumn vast numbers of eels moved downstream to the sea, where many were caught by fishermen awaiting their migration. But those eels that avoided capture moved out into the ocean, never to return, for no adult eel was ever seen returning to its freshwater home.

In the spring and summer of each succeeding year, after the adult eels' fall migration, tiny eel-like creatures appeared along the coast of Europe and moved through the Straits of Gibraltar into the Mediterranean. These young eels, or elvers, were incorrectly assumed to be the offspring of the adult eels that had gone down the rivers the previous autumn. Later the elvers entered the freshwater streams and rivers, moving upstream where they grew to maturity.

Scientists were puzzled as to how,

when, and where young eels were born, because the eggs of eels had never been found in the bodies of the adult females, and males of the species had never been seen.

It was not until 1777 that the ovary of the eel was first recognized by a professor of anatomy at the University of Bologna, thus definitely establishing an eel female sex. Ninety-five years later the scientific discovery of a male eel was announced.

In 1846, a German, Johann Jakob Kaup, found in the sea a small ribbon-like fish with a tiny head. Placing the creature in a bottle of alcohol, he labeled

Freshwater eel

it *Leptocephalus brevirostris;* after that the tiny creature was forgotten.

Half a century passed before two Italians, Gracci and Calandrucci, found one of Kaup's little fishes in the Mediterranean, but it was much larger and more fully developed. The Italian scientists identified their discovery as the young of the edible freshwater eel that inhabited the streams of the European continent. Thus, the stage was set for the Danish scientist, Johann Schmidt.

For 15 years, starting in 1906, Schmidt towed nets from the English Channel to Chesapeake Bay, and from Greenland to Puerto Rico, collecting and correlating the sizes of eel larvae. He reasoned that the larvae were growing as they moved toward their freshwater homes, away from the oceanic depths in which they were spawned. It followed, therefore, that the smaller the larvae found in any part of the ocean, the nearer such a specimen must be to the place where it was born. After years of tireless effort Schmidt was able to fix the breeding and spawning grounds of the European eel, *Anguilla vulgaris,* and the American species, *Anguilla rostrata,* within the latitudes 20° to 30° north and longitudes 60° to 78° west, near the Sargasso Sea, the warmest water in the mid-Atlantic. He further established that the European eel spawning beds overlapped those of the American species.

But this discovery uncovered only one phase in the life cycle of the eel. During the period of growth in the fresh waters of their home continents, eels are a uniform green to yellowish-brown above, shading to a pale dirty white beneath, and are called yellow eels. The migratory instinct asserts itself at the breeding stage in autumn, when freshwater eels are between the ages of 7 and 15 years, at which time the sides of their bodies take on a metallic sheen and their backs become a deep black. This is their breeding dress, and they are known then as silver eels.

Upon assuming this dress, the bodies of the females pass through certain other marked changes. Their snouts become sharp, the eyes larger, and the pectoral

Each autumn, female freshwater eels move down rivers to the sea

fins, just back of the gill slits, become more pointed. Although the females have been voracious eaters all their lives, they cease feeding at this time. Leaving the lakes and rivers in which they have lived, they move downstream to the sea. While these visible changes have been taking place, it is not until the females have reached salt water that their ovaries mature. Upon arriving in the bays and estuaries into which the freshwater streams empty, they are joined by the mature males that have been living there, and together they start the journey back to their birthplace.

It is not known how far below the surface migrating eels swim, but somewhere beyond the continental shelf they pass from the range of human observation. Neither is it known how long it takes them to reach their destination, but it has been estimated that the European eel requires about six months to make the crossing, swimming at the rate of one-half-mile per hour. As the migration from the European continent begins in early autumn, and spawning starts in early spring at the breeding grounds, this estimate seems to be justified.

Upon arrival at the breeding grounds near the Sargasso Sea, the European species shares its spawning beds, to some extent, with its American cousin, whose beds overlap its own and extend westward from it. From Labrador southward to Panama and the West Indies, the silver eels from America have journeyed to the rendezvous within one to two months after reaching salt water. Hundreds of fathoms below the seaweed-clogged surface of this tropical sea, the eggs of both species are spawned; the females each produce from 5 to 20 million transparent, almost colorless, tiny eggs.

A week or so after fertilization the eggs are hatched, and larvae of both species begin life. One-fourth of an inch, ribbonlike, and so transparent that newsprint can be read through their bodies,

Eels have been found in Swiss lakes 3,000 feet above sea level

Female eels clamber over waterfalls and surmount dams to reach their destination upstream

they float for a time from 600 to 900 feet below the surface. Later they rise into the upper layers of water and slowly move northward. Reaching the latitude of Bermuda, a separation occurs.

The larvae of the European species drift eastward with the Gulf Stream on their long journey back to their native shores, feeding on plankton as they go, while their tiny American relatives drift westward toward the coastline of America.

During their first summer of life the European larvae are found in the western Atlantic. By the second summer they have reached the central Atlantic, and by the third they have arrived off the coast of Europe. During their two and one-half years in the ocean, they attain a length of from two to three and one-half inches, but still retain their flat, leaflike larval form. They are now faced with a new way of life and must be prepared to meet it. They cease feeding, lose their larval teeth, shrink in depth and length, and become elvers, or little eels. While they are shaped like their parents in miniature, they are still transparent, and so are known as glass eels. The American eel has a shorter larval history, for it reaches its home shores and the elver stage in about one year.

After the transformation from larva to elver, the females of both the American and European species ascend the fresh-water streams to live until the moment when the migratory instinct drives them back to the sea. In these journeys upstream, they feed ravenously on fishes, worms, clams, snails and aquatic plants, travel through pipelines and sewers, clamber over waterfalls and surmount dams to reach their destination.

As female eels have been found in ponds having no outlets or inlets, some believe they travel overland to reach these waters, choosing nights when the grass is damp for the journey. But since there is no evidence to justify this presumption, their presence in these isolated waters is something of a mystery. They are at home in high as well as low altitudes, having been found in Swiss lakes 3,000 feet above sea level.

The males remain in the brackish waters of lagoons and estuaries, where they grow to maturity and await the downstream migration of the females.

Female eels average from 2 to 3½ or 4 feet in length; males average around 14 to 18 inches and never grow longer than 24 inches. The vertebrae of these fishes mark the only difference between the American and European species; the American has an average of 107 segments; the European eel averages 114.

Differing from their salt water cousins, both freshwater eel species have a lower jaw that projects beyond the upper jaw, and the large mouth gapes back to a point even with, or somewhat behind, the eyes. On the side of the neck there are gill slits with upper corners on a line with the center of the base of the pectoral fins. A single fin, soft and without spines, extends along the back, around the tip of the tail, and forward on the underside of the body. There is no separation into dorsal, caudal or anal fins as with many other fishes. After the third or fourth year of life, eels develop small scales that are embedded in the skin. These are covered with a coating of slimy mucus, which has given rise to the simile, "as slippery as an eel."

Perhaps the most intriguing part of the life cycle of this unusual fish is that neither European nor American elvers have ever been known to appear off the shores of any continent but their own. A cause for their distribution was advanced by Schmidt, who pointed out that the American eel spawns farther west and south than the European species. This, together with the movement of the ocean currents, must be considered as causes directing the two species to their respective sides of the ocean.

While much has been learned since the turn of the century of the habits of these sluggish fishes, much remains unexplained. No one has ever collected an adult freshwater eel far out at sea, and no one really knows their route, or at what depth they swim on their way to the breeding grounds, or how they die after the eggs have been laid (*See also under Fish*). —P.B.

EELGRASS

Other Common Names—Grass wrack
Scientific Name—*Zostera marina*
Family—Zosteraceae (pond weed family)
Range—Southern Greenland and southeastern Labrador to North Carolina; James Bay; the Pacific Coast of North America; also along Eurasian coasts
Habitat—Shallow seawater

One of the most important plants for waterfowl, eelgrass was once practically the sole food of great flocks of brant that wintered along the coast of North America. A disease very nearly exterminated the plant by 1931, and the brant declined with it. In recent years eelgrass has been coming back, with a consequent increase in brant.

Eelgrass is a marine herb, growing entirely underwater, with long, ribbonlike leaves. Growing in clumps, it is spread by creeping rootstocks. Ducks and geese eat the seed, or nutlet, the leaves, and the starchy root.

There is a freshwater plant, *Vallisneria americana*, known as eelgrass; it is also called wild and water celery. The freshwater plant is also valuable for the nourishment it affords waterfowl.

—G.B.S.

Eelgrass

EGRET (*For a general discussion of egrets, see under Heron*)

Cattle Egret

Other Common Names—Cattle heron
Scientific Name—*Bubulcus ibis*
Family—Ardeidae (herons and bitterns)
Order—Ciconiiformes
Size—Length, 20 to 27 inches
Range—Established in the western hemisphere beginning in 1877 when first noted in British Guiana, established in Venezuela, Colombia, and Surinam and nesting north to Florida, Louisiana, South Carolina, and New Jersey. Recorded elsewhere throughout much of the eastern United States, the Middle West, and in California. In Old World: Spain and Portugal, Africa, eastern Turkey and around Caspian Sea, east to India, Southeast Asia, and southern China; also Ceylon, Java, Bali south to Australia

The year 1952 witnessed an occurrence unprecedented in the history of American ornithology. For the first time a foreign bird, the cattle egret of the Old World—*Bubulcus ibis*—appeared numerously in the United States, without being introduced through human agency. Undoubtedly the birds came from the northern part of South America where they had lived for years previously. How they originally got to South America is a mystery. They may have arrived in the United States through Central America or, more likely, by direct flight across the Caribbean and the Gulf of Mexico to Florida.

One of the most interesting facts about this bird is the manner in which it was first recorded in the United States. Its definite existence here was established by an observer who, at the time, was unaware of his discovery. Though specimens of the cattle egret were not then secured, the birds were recorded on movie film from which, later, they were readily identified.

On March 12, 1952, Richard Borden,

One week old cattle egret chick in its nest at Drum Island, South Carolina

Cattle egret eggs are laid in a loosely constructed nest of twigs and grasses

The distribution of the cattle egret along the Gulf and Atlantic coasts

of Massachusetts, was photographing birds on the Eagle Bay Ranch, four miles south of Okeechobee City, Florida. He was particularly concerned with a group of white birds feeding among cattle and assumed they were snowy egrets.

On April 23, 1952, Richard Stackpole, William Drury, and Allen Morgan were afield in Sudbury Valley, Massachusetts, when they saw a strange bird that they

followed up and collected (shot for the scientific record and preserved as a museum specimen). It was a cattle egret. Later in the summer, these gentlemen were present at the showing of Borden's film of birds in Florida, and in one of the scenes they recognized the cattle egret. This was in the footage secured by Borden in March on the Eagle Bay Ranch and plainly showed the birds feeding with cattle. Therefore, Borden's pictures definitely established the cattle egret as occurring in Florida.

There is some evidence that cattle egrets were seen in Florida even earlier. In May of 1948 Willard H. Dilley, then of Clewiston, Florida and later on the staff of the Everglades National Park, saw a bird near his home that he thought was of this species. He concluded, naturally enough, that it was an escapee from some private or public collection, and therefore said nothing about it. In view of what has transpired since, however, this should be considered as the first sight record for the country.

Four years later, on June 1, 1952, Louis A. Stimson, of Miami, saw 10 cattle egrets near the Indian Prairie Canal, which empties into Lake Okeechobee, Florida.

During the summer of 1952 two cattle egrets appeared at Cape May, New Jersey, and were seen by many observers. One was also reported in the Chicago region some weeks later. In Florida, Stimson saw one bird near Lake Harbor on August 24, 1952, and four at the south shore of Lake Okeechobee on the 31st. A bird was noted near Cambridge, Massachusetts, along the Charles River, on November 27-28, and another was collected on the 28th at North Truro, Massachusetts.

It was the belief of experienced observers that the cattle egret had probably already nested in Florida and, if not, would certainly be doing so soon. This conviction was justified on May 5, 1953, when the first nest in North America was discovered in a heron rookery on an island in Lake Okeechobee. It contained one egg, and was photographed, together with birds on and near it. This discovery was duplicated later in the month when three more nests were found. It was estimated that there were at least a dozen pairs of cattle egrets nesting, but time limitations prevented detailed search for other nests. Thus was the cattle egret established as breeding in North America. The future of the cattle egret as a nesting species in the United States had apparently been assured.

In August 1956, T. L. Quay wrote: "One of the factors in the increasing spread of the cattle egret may be a high order of dominance in its relation to other herons." Quay gave as a reason for this belief the behavior of the two pairs at the rookery on Battery Island, North Carolina. Herbert Stoddard, a widely known biologist of Thomasville, Georgia, also mentioned this as early as 1954, and later observations at the "source" rookery in Lake Okeechobee, Florida, have borne out the beliefs of Stoddard and Quay.

There seems to be no particular competition between the cattle egret and the native North American herons, because the cattle egret in its feeding habits is largely a bird of uplands and open fields rather than marshes. It feeds much on insects and is an independent, vigorous bird, well able to take care of itself, without exhibiting an undue amount of pugnacity.

In general, the cattle egret resembles the snowy egret or an immature little blue heron, but it is stockier, has a stout, short, yellow or orange beak, and stands more erectly. Adult cattle egrets show a tawny wash on the neck and back. The legs are dark in winter and pale to a yellowish in spring. This may be a seasonal change, or perhaps an immature to adult transition.

If one wishes to see one of these birds, it should be looked for in pastures where cattle are grazing. The association between this bird and cattle is truly remarkable. No species was ever better named. Every step the cow takes is matched by the egret, the bird remaining only inches from the hoofs or nose of the animal. Now and then the cattle egret is pushed aside by the cow or steer and is often to be seen under the feeding animal's belly between the fore and hind legs. That it escapes being stepped upon is astonishing. The insects disturbed by

Cattle egret (immature, left; adult, right)

cattle are at once snapped up as the egrets make sudden dashes here and there to secure them. At times the egrets reach up and pick insects from the bodies of grazing cattle. Now and then the birds alight on the backs of the animals.

One peculiar characteristic of the cattle egret is a strange, wavy motion of the head and neck. The movement seems to flow down to and through the body—something like a prolonged letter S.

Every now and then a bird will stop, stand still, and indulge in this weaving behavior two or three times and then begin feeding again. —A.S., Jr.

Recommended Reading

Annual Report of the Smithsonian Institution (1954). Smithsonian Institution, Washington, D.C.
Audubon Magazine—July-August 1953; September-October 1953; March-April 1956; September-October 1956.

Common Egret
Other Common Names—American egret, white heron, white crane
Scientific Name—*Casmerodius albus*
Family—Ardeidae (herons and bitterns)
Order—Ciconiiformes
Size—Length, 41 inches
Range—Occurs on every continent. In the New World from southern Minnesota and Idaho, northern Ohio, and New Jersey south to Mexico, the West Indies, Central and South America. Wanders north to southern Canada

The first sight of a graceful snow-white common egret is well calculated to bring a thrill to the heart of any birdwatcher. Whether standing motionless in the shallow margins of lakes or lagoons, or leisurely winging its way to some distant swamp, there to perch in the top of a tall tree, the bird always attracts attention by its dazzling white stately form. Fairly abundant in many parts of its range, the common and the snowy egrets particularly were slaughtered from Florida and Louisiana to the Carolinas by plume hunters who sought the feathers because of the high prices paid for them by the millinery trade (*See also under Snowy Egret*). The National Audubon Society secured the passage of restrictive laws, outlawing the use of the feathers, and stationed wardens in egret rookeries to protect the birds. The egrets responded remarkably and are once again fairly numerous (*See under National Audubon Society*).

The plumes of the common egret are about 16 inches long and are about 50 in number. They are part of the breeding season adornment of the bird and appear only during the mating and nesting season.

The food of the common egret consists of fishes, frogs, crawfishes, lizards, and many insects, including locusts and grasshoppers. The nest, made in colonies, is a flimsy platform of sticks in bushes or trees, usually over water. From three to four bluish-green eggs are laid.

The common egret is easily observed against the lush green of a Georgia swamp

Reddish Egret
Other Common Names—None
Scientific Name—*Dichromanassa rufescens*
Family—Ardeidae (herons and bitterns)
Order—Ciconiiformes
Size—Length, 30 inches
Range—From southern Florida, the Gulf Coast, and Baja California, south to Hispaniola, Jamaica, and Yucatan

A "must" for the bird lister who visits the Florida Keys, is the reddish egret, *Dichromanassa rufescens*. One can usually manage to see at least one or two of these interesting birds, and visitors who are especially lucky may get a look at one in the white color phase, an even rarer experience in this region. They are observed with most regularity during their nesting season, which in this area is in winter and early spring. The only other place in the United States where one can be sure of observing them is on the Texas coast. Elsewhere, to see a reddish egret, one must go to certain parts of Mexico, Central America, or to Cuba, the Bahamas, a spot or two in Hispaniola or to a couple of small islands in the southern Caribbean. Even so, they are not abundant except locally and one would have to know in advance exactly where to look for them. The reddish egret is something of an anomaly. It is neither a rare species, in the sense that it is by no means so few in numbers as to belong in the threatened class, nor is it widely distributed or generally abundant. Originally this must have been quite a different story, for the species was abundant along the west coast of Florida prior to 1866, although today there are a considerable number of deserted nesting areas in this state. At the present time it cannot be said to be numerous except in south Texas. It differs in several respects from other wading birds. There is, for example, the fascinating polymorphic character that results in dark, white, and intermediate color phases.

To a considerable extent the range of the reddish egret is limited by the fact that it is essentially a saltwater, mangrove-nesting population, with the outstanding exception of the Texas colonies where the birds nest on dry islands grown with mesquite, yucca, and cacti. However, since frost is the chief limiting factor on the mangrove's growth, it is probable that during certain interglacial periods of the Pleistocene there was vigorous mangrove along the entire Gulf Coast. On the Florida peninsula, according to John H. Davis, Jr., low temperatures are effective in limiting mangrove growth as far south as Ft. Myers on the west coast and to Jupiter on the east coast. Few large mature mangrove swamps occur north of these points. It was probably otherwise during certain portions of the Pleistocene, or glacial period, the latest of the glacial epochs during which Canada, northern and northeastern U.S., northern and northwestern Europe, northern Asia, and most high mountains of the northern hemisphere were largely covered with ice. In recent times, since the end of the glacial period, the reddish egret nested in some numbers north to at least the Anclote River above Tampa Bay and to Pelican Island on the east coast. There are two records of freshwater nesting, at Orange Lake in 1911 and along the Kissimmee River in 1926, but these appear to have been completely "out of character."

Man has been responsible for reducing the range of the reddish egret quite drastically in Florida, and to some degree in Texas. When W. E. D. Scott visited Florida in the spring of 1880 he found a "particular abundance" of reddish egrets on the west coast, but upon his return in May 1886 a serious reduction in numbers had already resulted from the wholesale raids of the plume hunters. On May 8, Scott went to a rookery site between Pine Island and the mainland, just below Charlotte Harbor. Plumers had recently been there and the

The reddish egret (shown in both color phase

location was strewn with broken eggs and piles of dead birds. Vultures and fish crows hovered over the dismal scene. The reddish egret was the most common species in the piles of dead bodies, lying there half-decayed, their plumes, and sometimes their wings as well, stripped from them. Plume hunters that he met with in that region told Scott that they were after American, snowy, and reddish egrets "as they brought the highest prices." White phase reddish egrets— called "muffled-jawed egrets" by the plumers—were much in demand.

Among some 200 herons and egrets that were still alive in the Pine Island rookery there were a few reddish egrets, two of them in the white plumage. Near Punta Rassa several days later Scott saw a number of this species, widely scattered and very shy. Before the work of the plume hunters was done the reddish egret was to be driven out of this entire region, and they have not come back even yet, nearly 70 years later, except as rare stragglers. Today their breeding range in Florida is confined to a few mangrove keys in Florida Bay and they are seldom seen north of the vicinity of Cape Sable. Alexander Sprunt, Jr., saw one at the Pearce Ranch on the Kissimmee River, February 22, 1947, and another at Boca Grande, near Charlotte Harbor, on March 9, 1950. A small number of them may have continued to breed through the years in remote parts of Florida Bay. In his report for the year 1904, Audubon Warden Guy Bradley estimated that there were 300 of this species in the region from Key West north to the mainland of Florida and up the west coast as far as Chokoloskee

In 1905 H. Job saw the species in eastern Florida Bay near Tavernier and the following year Mrs. Lucas Brodhead found it "not uncommon" on Upper Matecumbe Key. On March 29, 1908, with A. H. Bent and Louis Agassiz Fuertes, Frank M. Chapman saw six reddish egrets at the head of Snake Bight, "fishing . . . in their eager, alert, graceful way." Today it is a regular breeder at a number of locations, but the entire Florida population may not exceed 150.

By the summer of 1950 the Green Island Colony had dropped off to about 1,400 pairs and there were only four outer colonies, each of which was smaller than in 1939. During these years there has been a rapidly increasing amount of human activity on the Texas coast and it would appear that a combination of adverse factors and influences has brought about this gradual loss of population. In spite of this situation, the fact remains that Green Island is the one location in the entire range where the reddish egret numbers in the thousands. Two geographic races have been described in Mexico, where the Texas birds undoubtedly winter.

Of all the engaging characteristics of this bird, however, none seems to be of greater interest than the fact that it appears in different color phases. For many years it was thought that the white phase was a separate species—Peale's egret, described from a Florida specimen in 1828 by Charles Lucien Bonaparte. This was in line with the species concept that prevailed until fairly recently. Biologists working in the field of the evolution of species have recently pointed out that so much progress has been made in the field of genetics over the last 30 or 40 years that nearly 100 so-called species of birds alone have been shown to be merely genetic variants of polymorphic species. In other words, color variation in birds like the reddish egret and reef heron is presumably controlled by the relationship of dominant and recessive genes and their respective frequencies in the various populations. And there is more to this than academic interest. The variable character—in this case the white, dark, or intermediate plumage color—rarely has selective value as such. But this same character is the visual expression of a gene that may also control unseen physiological processes having favorable or unfavorable selective value. We do not know, for example, if white phase or dark phase reddish egrets are the most successful (although there seem to be more dark birds now than formerly, perhaps because the white ones were most sought after by the plume hunters). The color of the plumage by itself, however, may or may not be important in survival. But dark birds, one can theorize, may result from gene distributions and frequencies that also produce greater vigor. The viability factors themselves are affected: longevity, sexual activity, fecundity, resistance to environmental and climatic pressures, etc. Obviously, there is much yet to be learned and we are only at the threshold of ornithological knowledge in these vital fields, but it is clear that polymorphism has a far deeper significance than appears on the surface.

If we are really to understand such important species as the reddish egret and continue to provide for their welfare in an increasingly difficult world, we must not be blind to any possibilities, least of all to those that may teach us how to plan intelligently and surely for their ultimate survival. So, the next time you add a reddish egret to your list make careful notes as to its exact plumage characteristics. There can be more to birding than merely that which meets the eye. Every bird on one's personal list has a fascinating background of special problems that constitute the real meat of modern ornithology. Therein lies a world of absorbing interest and the door stands wide open.   —R.P.A.

Snowy egrets nest in the low branches of trees or near the ground in marsh vegetation

Snowy Egret
Other Common Names — Snowy heron
Scientific Name — *Leucophoyx thula*
Family — Ardeidae (herons and bitterns)
Order — Ciconiiformes
Size — Length, 24 inches
Range — Northern California, southeastern Idaho to Colorado, central Oklahoma and the Gulf Coast. Nests from Cape May, New Jersey, south through Florida, West Indies, to Chile and central Argentina. Wanders northward to southern Canada, Wisconsin, southern Michigan, New Brunswick, and Newfoundland. Winters from South Carolina and California southward

No other bird in this country offers such a dramatic conservation lesson as the snowy egret: it is the story of a beautiful bird persecuted to the brink of extinction and then saved.

A hundred years ago the snowy egret was an abundant species. That was before the days of the feather trade. But both the tall common, or American, egret and the dainty little snowy egret are adorned with sprays of beautiful white plumes that cascade gracefully from their backs. There grew a demand for these feathers, a demand that nearly wiped out the species.

Like so many other water-loving birds,

Snowy egret in a shallow pond stirs the bottom with its foot to flush out food

egrets prefer to nest in colonies of a dozen or even hundreds of individuals. These "bird cities" are usually widely spaced, therefore it was easy for the plume hunters to shoot them out one by one.

The plume hunters located colonies by watching the direction the snowy egrets took in flying to and from their feeding grounds. Sometimes the hunters searched for days or weeks to locate the heronry in the heart of some moss-hung swamp. Once its location was known, the colony was doomed.

It was only the spray of delicate white plumes, which attains its greatest perfection during the breeding season, that was wanted. Plume hunters ripped these from the fallen bird's back and the broken body was left to float on the murky water of the swamp. The young in the nests were left to starve.

When the plume hunter departed, few birds remained alive. A scene of beauty was changed to one of dreary desolation. In a short while a stench of dead egrets arose from the swamp and the white bodies slowly sank into the mire.

Fortunately, a public opinion strong enough to outlaw this feather trade was created by the National Association of Audubon Societies, now called the National Audubon Society, and organized for the protection of egrets and other persecuted birds. But laws without enforcement are of little use, so Audubon wardens were placed on guard over the few remaining birds. During those first few years two of the Audubon wardens were killed and others were wounded in gun battles with plume hunters. (*See Guy Bradley under National Audubon Society*)

Since those troubled days, organized killing has stopped and the birds have increased. Tens of thousands now nest in Audubon sanctuaries and elsewhere. There is real encouragement in this experience. It proves that Audubon conservation is not mere theory—it works.

Unfortunately, however, time has a habit of bringing new problems, and today's conservation tasks seem at least as complex and difficult as the fight against the plume hunters was to the founders of Audubon societies. Today it is space and water that must be fought for; air and water pollution, greed and short-sightedness that must be opposed.

—A.S., Jr.

Recommended Reading

A Glance Backward—John K. Terres. *Audubon Magazine* July-August 1952.
Adventures in Bird Protection—T. Gilbert Pearson. Appleton-Century-Crofts, Inc., New York, New York.

ELK
Other Common Names—Wapiti
Scientific Name—*Cervus canadensis*
Family—Cervidae (deer family)
Order—Artiodactyla
Size—Male: body length, 7½ to 9½ feet; height at shoulder, 4½ to 5 feet; weight, 700 to 900 pounds. Females slightly smaller
Range—The Rocky Mountains from northern New Mexico to Alberta, Manitoba, and central Saskatchewan; Vancouver Island and northwestern Washington, south to northwestern California, and southeastern Oregon

The elk, or wapiti, is the largest member of the North American deer family with the exception of the moose. Elk once ranged over much of the northern two-thirds of the United States—from the Berkshires and southern Appalachians to the Pacific Coast (except in the Great Basin) and from northern Alberta to southern New Mexico. With the settlement of this continent they diminished rapidly in number and completely disappeared from the eastern states at an early date.

Today the great stronghold for the elk, *Cervus canadensis*, is Yellowstone National Park, but a fair number are found in Montana, Idaho, Washington, Manitoba, the Olympic Peninsula of the United States, and a few in northern British Columbia.

Popular names of animals at times may be confusing. The name, elk, was first used and still is used for the Old World moose. Wapiti is said to be the name for the American elk used by the Shawnee Indians.

Elk are more or less sociable and have a tendency to band together in herds. In the early winter when they move down from the mountains to avoid the deep snows, small groups come together and form relatively large herds. In winter these large animals browse on sage, juniper, Douglas-fir, and aspen twigs. During this time the bulls lose their

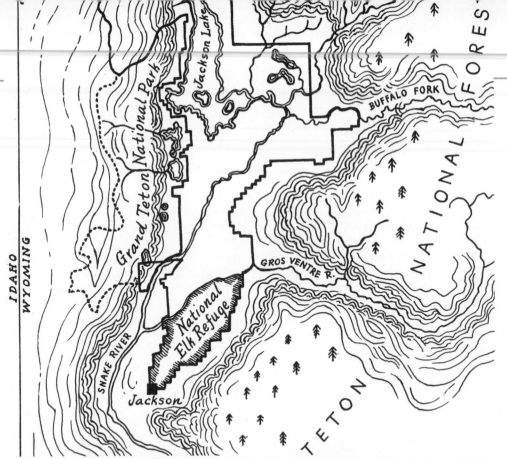

National Elk Refuge is located at the southern end of Jackson Hole, Wyoming

Elk, or wapiti

antlers. In spring the elk will start once more for the high alpine meadows and a diet of grasses, sedges, and dandelions. The bulls, with their new, growing antlers, usually lead the way. Later the cows will follow with their newborn calves. These spotted youngsters remain with their mothers until the following spring.

All summer, elk are spread out over the mountain ridges at an elevation high enough to avoid the flies and other biting insect pests. Usually several cows and calves accompanied by two or three bulls form a family group and it is not unusual to see 15 or 20 stags together in a sort of "bachelors' club." Only during the rutting season is there discord among these antlered monarchs. In general behavior the elk is typically deerlike. The bulls are polygamous and the call, or *bugle*, during the mating season is a battle challenge to any other males in the neighborhood.

After polishing their heavy antlers and staging mock fights, the bulls are ready for actual combat. Furious charges may result in locked antlers, but usually the fight ends with the victor leading away his newly won harem of cows.

The dwarf elk, tule elk, or California elk, *Cervus nannodes*, is a smaller and paler animal than *Cervus canadensis*. At one time it was almost extinct; today it exists in the wild only in Owens Valley, Kern County, and Inyo County, California.   —G.G.G.

ELM

The elm family, Ulmaceae, is widely distributed in the northern hemisphere. It includes trees with elliptical toothed leaves and purple or green flowers in small clusters in their axils. The flowers of elms are often eaten by purple finches and gray squirrels; the winged seeds are also a favorite food of squirrels. Besides the elms, the family includes the 50 or 60 species of hackberry trees, *Celtis*.

The American elm, which grows to a height of 120 feet, is a graceful orna-

mental. Its native habitat is swampland, and introducing it to upland roadsides and parks has resulted in a weakness and lack of resistance to the beetleborne fungus wilt called Dutch elm disease.

Slippery elm, cork elm, and winged elm are also eastern trees. The family is well represented in the West by the many hackberries, some of which become large trees while others are shrubby. They are commonly planted for shade and ornament in the Middle West. The orange to black fruit of the hackberries was one of the staple foods of the western Indians. The hackberry fruits (drupes) are much eaten by birds, especially in winter. The fruits are favorites of the cedar waxwing, yellow-bellied sapsucker, mockingbird, and robin.   —G.B.S.

American Elm
Other Common Names—White elm, gray elm, water elm, swamp elm, soft elm
Scientific Name—*Ulmus americana*
Family—Ulmaceae (elm family)
Range—Southern Newfoundland and southern Ontario to eastern Saskatchewan and Maine to North Dakota; south to central Texas and central Florida
Habitat—Beside water courses, in pastures, and along streets
Leaves—Two to six inches long, oval, moderately pointed with coarse, forward-curving teeth and a lopsided base. They are arranged alternately on the stem; the undersurface shows prominent, parallel veins
Bark—Flaky yellow-gray or ashy-gray and brown, seldom very thick, with shallow to moderately deep, irregular vertical grooving, broadly ridged, covered with fine scales
Flowers—Small (one inch) sprays of three to four tiny hanging blossoms, in short-stalked clusters, olive or rusty, burst from fattened winter buds early in spring
Fruit—Greenish or reddish, fuzzy, flattened oval seeds each surrounded by a marginal "wing," which is split and toothed at the bottom one-half inch across

This large, vase-shaped tree is probably familiar to more North Americans than any other single species of tree. Yet the American elm did not occupy a prominent place in the original North American forests and was confined largely to the banks of streams, lakes, and marshes where it still grows. Today, however, people tend to think of elms as gracing a roadside or a pasture, or arching over a New England or midwestern city street. Washington, D. C. is said to be the most elm-planted city in America.

The Baltimore oriole, *Icterus galbula*, always makes its purselike nest at the very tips of elm branches. There, where no four-footed creature can disturb them, they set about raising their young each year. To see one of these nests swinging in the summer breeze and to hear the clear whistling of the Baltimore oriole is a cheering experience (*See under Oriole*).

If the Baltimore oriole is attached to the American elm, it is no more so than the people who belong to elm clubs and associations. These devotees to their preservation regularly go about searching for old elms. American elms 140 feet high, with trunks 11 feet in diameter, have been recorded; however, a more usual size would be 100 feet tall with a 5-foot trunk buttressing out at the base to 10 or 15 feet. Long before white men came to America, elms were council trees for Indian tribes. Later, both white and red men met under elms to make their treaties.

Despite its impressive size the American elm is victimized by a fungus that lives in its water-conducting vessels. The tiny spores of this fungus spread rapidly throughout the tree and cause wilting, yellowing, and dropping of the elm leaves. The tree may die in a few weeks; may gradually succumb over a period of years, or may recover. This fungus, known as the Dutch elm disease, *Graphum ulmi*, was introduced from Europe in the 1920's and is transmitted from tree to tree by the elm bark beetle.

Since the elm bark beetle lives in the bark of dead and dying elms, one means of controlling the Dutch elm disease is to burn all dead trees and fallen elm branches.

Sometimes the leaves of American elms look tattered from the nibblings of inchworms and leafhoppers, but this destruction is not to be confused with the Dutch elm disease. Often a tree is needlessly destroyed by a well-meaning person. Before destroying an elm suspected of having the disease, one should send twigs of the tree to the State Department of Agriculture for inspection by experts.

The value of elm trees in supplying food for wildlife is not as great as oaks, maples, and dogwoods. Nevertheless, the seeds or buds are eaten considerably by wood ducks, grouse, pheasants, wild turkeys, purple finches, rose-breasted grosbeaks, and other birds. There are six or seven native species of elm, primarily in the eastern United States—the slippery elm, cedar elm, Florida elm, rock elm, and others.   —G.A.B.

ENCEPHALITIS

Encephalitis is a generic term for a disorder of the central nervous system and may have many causes. The disease causes an inflammation of the brain. It is popularly known as sleeping sickness. Measles and mumps, if inadequately treated, may produce disturbances properly called encephalitic. But discussed here is only the insect-borne, virus-induced encephalitis. The diagnosis of this disease requires slow and expensive laboratory testing. There are even several types of insect-borne encephalitis (representing different virus "populations") in the United States, such as eastern equine encephalitis (EEE), western equine (WEE), St. Louis (SLE), with other strains present in many other places, especially in warm countries.

American elm

The viruses may be present in a number of animal populations, including snakes, small mammals, and birds. The first isolation of one of these viruses occurred in horses, hence the name equine encephalitis. The present emphasis on birds as carriers may turn out to be as premature as the conclusion that this was a disease of horses transmittable to man.

Nevertheless, birds are among those groups already known to carry certain insect-borne viruses of encephalitis. In fact, birds are known to carry antibodies, indicating that they have had the disease themselves at one point in their lives, perhaps as nestlings. But viremia (active, transmittable virus in the blood stream) is rarely encountered, indicating that the disease is of short duration in birds—they either die quickly or recover quickly.

Given a *reservoir* of live virus in *carriers*—whether in birds or other animals —there must be a means of transmitting it from one animal to another in order for the disease to spread. Penned pheasants will pass it from one to another by pecking, but most spreading is usually done by small biting animals, whether mosquitoes, ticks, or other insects, and these insects are called *vectors.*

The best protection against local outbreaks of encephalitis, at the present time, appears to be maintaining sentinel flocks of chickens which public health authorities can watch for incidence of the disease. High levels of viremia in the sentinel flock may be a warning that the disease could overflow from wild populations to humans, and the most practical defense, then, becomes one of mosquito abatement, since these insects are the most common vector of the disease.   —R.C.C.

ENZYME

Enzymes are the many and various compounds, produced by living cells, that promote changes in other substances without being changed themselves.

They apparently control all of the vital processes on the level of the cell, all of those that involve living protoplasm. Without them, life, as we know it, could not exist. Enzymes promote the conversion of plant starches into sugars, animal glucose into carbon dioxide and water, and all the other processes of digestion and metabolism.

The exact composition of enzymes and their molecular arrangement is imperfectly known. Although their functions may be observed, science has been unable to explain why they perform as they do.   —G.B.S.

EPIPHYTE

These are the plants that grow upon the outer surface of other plants, using their hosts as supports, but never robbing them of nourishment. They are never harmful to the live trees they attach themselves to, unless they grow in such profusion as to cut off light from the leaves of the trees, or overburden its branches with their combined weight.

The roots of epiphytes, or air plants as they are often called, are used to keep a secure grip on the bark of the trees, poles, or other stationery objects they cling to, and to collect moisture from the air and from rainwater. Epiphytes utilize the chemical compounds that are results of the decaying of the bark of the host trees, but otherwise their raw materials are derived entirely from air and sunlight.

Most epiphytes live in moist regions. Spanish "moss," also called Florida moss, one of the commonest members of the pineapple family, is a common epiphyte in the Southeast. This picturesque plant forms gray-green festoons on trees and is especially abundant on cypresses, and live oaks from Virginia to Texas.

Closely related to Florida moss are the various species of the so-called air "pines," or *Tillandsia,* that live as epiphytes on trees from Georgia to Florida. Air pines even form colonies on telephone

Tillandsia *is a common epiphyte from Georgia to Florida*

Spanish moss and Tillandsia *are epiphytic, or air plants*

wires, forming tufts that resemble birds' nests.

Orchids, ferns, mosses, bromeliads (pineapple family), and cacti are frequently epiphytic in the tropics. In temperate North America mosses and ferns commonly occur as epiphytes in swamps.

—G.B.S.

ERYTHRIN (*See under Animal: Colors of Animals*)

ERYTHRISM (*See under Albinism*)

EUCALYPTUS
Tasmanian Blue Eucalyptus
Other Common Names — Blue gum
Scientific Name — *Eucalyptus globulus*
Family — Myrtaceae (myrtle family)
Range — Native of Tasmania; introduced from Australia. Widely planted in California, southern Arizona, New Mexico, the Gulf Coast of Texas, and in Florida
Habitat — The most common of many eucalypti planted for cordwood and windbreaks in the semiarid regions of the United States
Leaves — 6 to 12 inches long, leathery, and curved like a sickle. They drop off at irregular intervals and have stems and twigs square in cross section with a tendency to twist about. (Near midday the leaves turn their edges toward the scorching sun, apparently a response that conserves moisture)
Bark — Outer bark is thin, reddish-brown, and peels off in long strips, revealing a smooth, creamy-white or gray underbark
Flowers — Flattened white puffballs with dark centers

Fruit — Unmistakable, rather boxlike with bluntly pointed tops and, when ripe, a mahogany color coated with powdery white. The more pointed outer cap is shed, leaving a flat, disklike end

Of the nearly 140 species of eucalyptus, all native to Australia, only the blue gum is commonly planted in the United States. This tree has been so success-

Eucalyptus

fully introduced — especially in California — that it grows by the millions in some areas.

The blue gum attains a height up to 200 feet with a slender trunk seldom more than a yard in diameter at its base. Its long, narrow, waxy blue leaves are attached to slender branches that droop downward and give the effect that the tree is covered with feathers. Because of the continual shredding of the bark, the trunk always has a shaggy appearance, especially in older trees.

In its native Australian habitat, the eucalyptus often grows where no water is apparently available. But its roots grow deeply, seeking out the meager ground water, and the tree thrives. For this reason it is often planted in semiarid regions of North America as a windbreak tree along fields and roads. It is not a particularly good choice for the city, because, like the cottonwood, it interferes with drainage pipes (*See Cottonwood; also Poplar*).

The eucalyptus is also used for fuel wood and one authority says that 1/10 acre of trees 10 or 12 years old will furnish a continuous supply of cord-wood for a family since the tree can be pruned heavily.

Both the leaves and the bark have commercial value. The oil of eucalyptus leaves is used in a variety of medicinal preparations, and the bark yields tannin in large quantities.

Related eucalyptus trees include the sugar gum, the big red gum, *Eucalyptus rostrata*, and the lemon-scented gum, *Eucalyptus citriodora*, noted for its fine appearance and fragrant leaves. These species are sometimes planted as ornamental trees.

All of the eucalyptus species that have been introduced in the United States have a characteristic shape that is quite pleasing to the eye. Fortunately a beetle that eats the terminal buds of these trees and causes them to develop a bunchy, unpleasing profile has been effectively barred from the United States because only the seeds of these species have been introduced. —G.A.B.

Recommended Reading

Trees: The Yearbook of Agriculture, 1949—U.S. Department of Agriculture, Washington, D.C.

EVENING PRIMROSE
Common Evening Primrose
Other Common Names—Night willow herb
Scientific Name—*Oenothera biennis*
Family—Onagraceae (evening primrose family)
Range—Newfoundland and Cote Nord, Quebec, to southeastern Alberta, south to Nova Scotia, New England, Long Island, northern Florida, Tennessee, Arkansas, North Dakota, and other states
Habitat—Dry, open soil
Time of Blooming—June to October

Evening primrose is an apt name for this plant as the inch-wide, yellow-petaled flowers open only (unless the day

Common evening primrose

is cloudy) in the late afternoon and remain open during the night and early morning. Moths and an occasional hummingbird visit the sweet-scented flowers in search of nectar. The fragrance of the flowers reminds one of the scent of lemons or limes. Sometimes the pronghorn antelope feeds on the plant of some species of evening primrose.

The evening primrose lives only two years. The first year it produces a rosette of leaves, which hug the ground during the winter; the following year it flowers, produces seeds, and then dies. The flowering stalk is from one to six feet high and much branched. The flowers grow from the axils of the leaves and, like most members of this family, have four petals, eight stamens, and a four-parted stigma. The leaves are slightly rounded at the base, notched, and lance-shaped and grow all the way up on the flower stalk. The petals of the flowers are attached at the top of the ovary instead of at the bottom, the more usual way. This is one of the characteristics of the evening primrose family that makes their members easy to recognize.

Late in the 19th century, the Dutch botanist Hugo de Vries noted the many variations among the evening primroses growing in his garden. His observations led to his great discovery, the phenomenon of evolution through mutation.

Large Desert Evening Primrose
Other Common Names — None
Scientific Name — *Oenothera deltoides*
Family — Onagraceae (evening primrose family)
Range — Deserts of southern California and adjacent Arizona
Habitat — Sandy places, lower Sonoran Zone
Time of Blooming — March to May

Large desert evening primrose

The large, new flowers of the desert evening primrose are white, but in a day or so they turn to pink. The petals open in late afternoon, closing by noon the next day. The plant does not grow very high but has many leaves and many woolly buds. The stems are very thick and wider at the base. When the plant dries up the branches come together at the top, making a sort of basket. The wind rolls this basket along over the ground like a tumbleweed, and the seeds are scattered in many new places.

EVERGLADES NATIONAL PARK
Location — Southern tip of Florida
Size — 2,100 square miles
Mammals — Cougars, black bears, deer, otters, raccoons, opossums, skunks, manatees, porpoises
Birdlife — Bald eagles, roseate spoonbills, wood storks, limpkins, herons, white-crowned pigeons, swallow-tailed kites, in winter, white pelicans, ducks, songbirds
Plants — Mangroves on coast, saw grass in glades, tropical hardwoods (mahogany, poisonwood, gumbo limbo) and pine on hammocks; royal and other palms

The Everglades is actually a river, about 200 miles long and about 60 miles wide, but only a few inches deep. It flows over a gently tilting limestone plateau from Lake Okeechobee to Florida Bay. Saw grass is the dominant plant, flourishing in the shallow soil, with its roots in the water.

Much of the park is in Florida Bay, where red mangroves, standing in the salt water, provide rookeries for ibises, herons, egrets, and other wading birds that nest there, often in the thousands. Some of Florida's waning population of bald eagles have also found refuge in the park.

Accommodations — At Flamingo, park headquarters on Florida Bay
Headquarters — Within the park

Western boundary of Everglades National Park, Florida

An osprey nests in a solitary mangrove in Everglades National Park, Florida

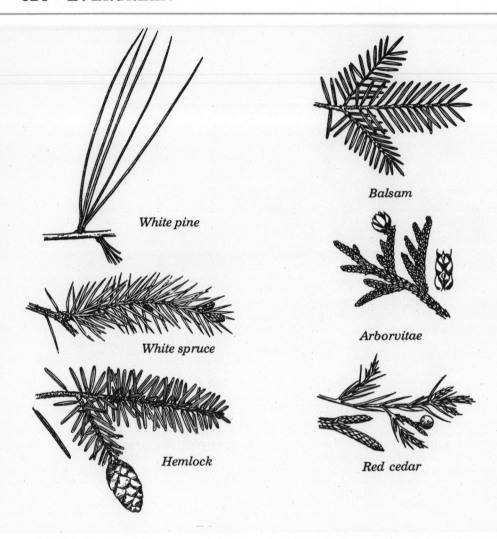

White pine

Balsam

White spruce

Arborvitae

Hemlock

Red cedar

EVERGREEN

Many plants remain green throughout the year. Since there is no regular period during which the leaves of such plants fall, they are always clothed with foliage —they are evergreen. Most of the conifers—pines, spruces, hemlocks, cedars, and other needle-leaved trees—are evergreens, and so are the broad-leaved evergreens—for example mountain laurel, rhododendron, and holly. Two needle-leaved trees that are exceptions are the larch and the bald cypress—conifers that shed their needles in the fall (*See also under individual entries: Arborvitae; Fir; Hemlock; Holly; Pine; Spruce; etc.; also*

Cypress: Bald Cypress; and under Fern).

Some Common Native Evergreens

The leaves of conifers are slender and are called needles. They have thick protective outside coats and exude very little moisture. The branches are elastic and the needles shed the snow much more easily than broad leaves.

Pines (*Pinus*). The leaves grow in bundles of two, three, or five and many have a sheathing scale at the base where the leaves join the twig. Common native pines are white pine (five needles in a bundle) and pitch pine (three needles in a bundle).

Spruces (*Piceae*). The leaves grow singly on the twigs; they are stiff, mostly four-sided, and pointed. Each needle rests on a little scale, or shelf, that stands out from the twig. White spruce, red spruce, and black spruce are the most common native spruces.

Hemlock (*Tsuga canadensis*). The leaves grow singly on the twigs, are soft and flat, and have distinct short stalks, or petioles. There are two white lines on the underside of each leaf and the tip is blunt. The twigs have a flat, featherlike appearance.

Balsam or balsam fir (*Abies balsamea*). The leaves grow singly on the twigs, are dark green, lustrous above, and are blunt, flat, and without stalk or petiole, although much constricted at the base. Like the hemlock, the leaves are usually arranged to give a flat appearance to the twig and each needle has two white lines on the underside.

Arborvitae (*Thuja occidentalis*). The leaves of arborvitae, or northern white cedar, have a very characteristic spicy odor, are bright green and have overlapping scales, close-pressed to the twig. The branches have a flat, fan-shaped appearance.

Red cedar (*Juniperus virginiana*). Leaves mostly scalelike, small, dark green or brownish-green, but needle-shaped, sharp-pointed leaves are produced on young trees or vigorous shoots.

Broad-leaved Evergreen Trees and Shrubs

Most broad-leaved trees and shrubs are deciduous. Since the leaves are not protected for winter life, they die in the fall and drop off the trees (maple, apple, elm). Some broad-leaved plants have protective adaptations against loss of water and the leaves remain on the trees throughout the winter. The leaves of such plants are protected by being small, having waxy, leathery, hairy, or thick-skinned covering, or by combining two or more of these characters. Some of these are:

Holly (*Ilex opaca*). A small tree. The

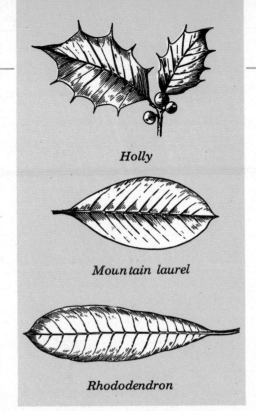

Holly

Mountain laurel

Rhododendron

leaves are shining green with spiny teeth and wavy margins and have a prominent midrib beneath. In holly trees, the so-called "female" trees have the red ornamental berries. These trees still need protection from people cutting the berry-covered branches in the wild. Fortunately, nursery-grown American holly trees are widely planted in gardens and estates and this has helped preserve them.

Mountain laurel (*Kalmia latifolia*). A common wild shrub. The leaves are leathery, deep lustrous green above, paler beneath, drooping and crowded at the tips of the branches. Some states have passed laws to protect the laurel from those who would cut its white-flowered branches in spring or its green leaves for decoration.

Rhododendron (*Rhododendron maximum*). A large shrub. The leaves are thick, lustrous green, often rusty beneath, with curled back edges. The lower the temperature, the tighter the leaves curl to prevent loss of water from the lower surface that, in these leaves, is the evaporating surface.

1. Loblolly Pine *Pinus taeda*
2. Long-leaf Pine *Pinus australis*
3. Short-leaf Pine *Pinus echinata*
4. Piñon Pine *Pinus cembroides var. edulis*
5. Norway Pine *Pinus resinosa*
6. Scrub Pine *Pinus virginiana*
7. Pitch Pine *Pinus rigida*
8. Ponderosa Pine (Western Yellow) *Pinus ponderosa*

9. Scotch Pine *Pinus sylvestris* (native of Europe and Asia)
10. Eastern White Pine *Pinus Strobus*
11. Lodgepole Pine *Pinus contorta var. Murrayana*
12. Noble Fir *Abies nobilis*
13. Balsam Fir *Abies balsamea*
14. White Fir *Abies concolor*

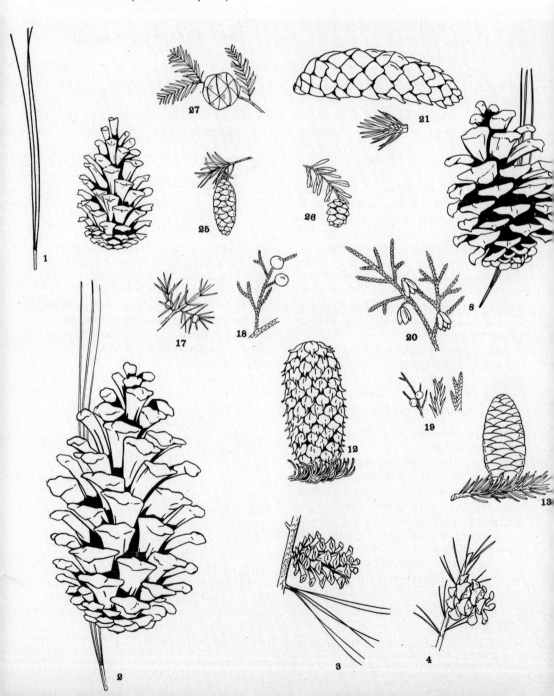

15. **Larch (Tamarack)** *Larix laricina*
16. **Pacific Yew** *Taxus brevifolia*
    (*Taxus canadensis*, a similar eastern species)
17. **Common Juniper** *Juniperus communis*
18. **Sierra (Western) Juniper** *Juniperus occidentalis*
19. **Eastern Red Cedar** *Juniperus virginiana*
20. **Northern White Cedar (Arbor Vitae)**
    Thuja occidentalis
21. **Norway Spruce** *Picea Abies* (European)

22. **Red Spruce** *Picea rubens*
23. **White Spruce** *Picea glauca*
24. **Douglas Fir** *Pseudotsuga taxifolia*
25. **Mountain Hemlock** *Tsuga Mertensiana*
26. **Eastern Hemlock** *Tsuga canadensis*
27. **Bald Cypress** *Taxodium distichum*
    (loses needles each fall — becomes "bald")
28. **Big Tree** *Sequoia gigantea*
29. **Coast Redwood** *Sequoia sempervirens*

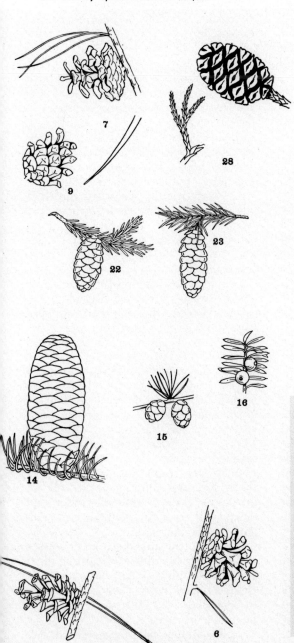

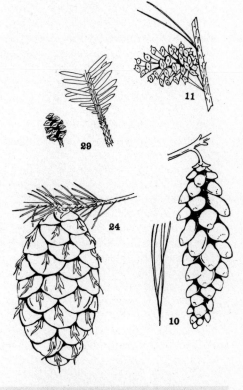

TIPS ON RECOGNITION

P is for Pine and P is for Package; pine needles come in packages of two or more.

S is for Spruce and S is for Square; spruce needles are four-angled, roll between fingers, are on pegs which make twigs feel rough.

F is for Fir and F is for Flat; fir needles are flat, do not roll easily between fingers; twigs feel smooth (no pegs).

Hem is for "Hem" lock and rhymes with stem' hemlock needles are flat but each has a tiny "stem" attached to a peglike base.

EVOLUTION (*See under Amphibian*)

EXTINCT AND THREATENED ANIMALS OF NORTH AMERICA

The Heath Hen

On a misty morning in March 1932, two government conservationists sat huddled in the lower pasture of James Green's farm on Martha's Vineyard, Massachusetts. A fog had rolled in from the ocean, blanketing the scrubby field, but through their binoculars they could see the unmistakable outline of a reddish-brown bird in a small clearing. Its tail was cocked and square, its head was tawny olive, and its neck showed tufts of hairlike feathers. It took a few mincing steps and uttered a long, resonant *whooo-ooo*.

The sound died slowly. The bird paused, as if it were waiting for a reply. In times past, the sandy flats of the Vineyard had echoed and reechoed with the hollow mating call. Now there was no answer. The bird flew upward and vanished into the swirling fog. The two men were the last to see what had once been one of America's most abundant birds—the famous heath hen. The heath hen, *Tympanuchus cupido cupido*, of the eastern United States, was a subspecies of the prairie chickens of our western prairies (*See under Chicken*).

The passing of the heath hen concluded another chapter in the story of extinction of certain species of American wildlife that began with the settlement of the North American continent. The pioneers on the American frontier saw a wilderness teeming with riches and believed its resources could never be exhausted. From the time of the first landings of white immigrants on the eastern seaboard to the eventual westward occupation of the entire land mass, our wildlife has been endangered, not only by overshooting and the belief that wildlife was inexhaustible but by changes in the use of the land, for example, the cutting of forests to convert them to cropland.

Through past ages (particularly at the end of the Mesozoic Era and during the Ice Age) countless animals have passed out of existence. Their passing, however, was a natural occurrence, a part of the long pattern of changes in climate and of evolution. But during our lifetime on this continent, we have witnessed extinction brought on, not by natural factors, but by the activities of man.

The Great Auk

One of the first North American birds to be lost forever because of man was the great auk, *Pinguinus impennis*, a flightless bird with back feathers of iridescent black, and breast feathers gleaming white and spotless. In the water it was a fast swimming and diving bird, but on land its flipperlike wings were useless. Awkward and without defenses, it was slow to move, and unused to any animal that could threaten it on the remote rocky islands and cliffs of its home in the northern hemisphere.

The great auk in North America lived along the craggy coastal regions of the Atlantic Ocean, the shores of the Maritime Provinces, Labrador, and Newfoundland. First noticed by French fishermen in 1497, it was slaughtered by the thousands for food, salted and stored in barrels. Jacques Cartier, on his expedition in 1534, reported that the great auk provided each of his ships sustenance for the return voyage. In later years, when women's styles demanded bright boas and brilliant plumes, the great auk was despoiled for its feathers. Hunting parties set out from the eastern seaboard cities and descended upon the helpless bird with guns, sticks, and nets.

For the great auk there was no place to hide. Whole colonies of nesting birds and young alike were wiped out in single frenzied hunts. Denied the chance to reproduce, the great auk population dwindled.

Well-meaning but short-sighted mu-

A rare photograph of an Eskimo curlew sighted in Texas in 1962

seum curators, recognizing the bird's plight, sponsored expeditions to capture the few great auks that remained. In June of 1884 a boatload of Icelandic fishermen landed on the offshore island of Eldey and wrung the necks of the only two birds that could be found. The great auk was never seen again.

The Labrador Duck

Other species, as similarly vulnerable to man's attacks on them, also disappeared. Such a species was the Labrador duck, *Camptorhynchus labradorium*. Like the great auk, it inhabited the American coastal regions of the Atlantic, but restricted its nesting areas to the shore of the Gulf of St. Lawrence and the coastline of Labrador. Unlike the great auk, the disappearance of the Labrador duck was sudden. In the mid-1880's, naturalists discovered to their surprise that the bird was waning, and within a few short years it had disap-

peared altogether. The last reported sighting occurred near Long Island, New York, in 1875.

The Labrador duck's demise was perplexing. It had not been sought out as a gamebird, nor was it coveted for its black and white plumage. Was it, perhaps, that the intrusion of man upon its nesting grounds destroyed the bird's normal pattern of behavior and brought it to extinction?

The Passenger Pigeon

It was the great abundance of the passenger pigeon, *Ectopistes migratorius*, however, that led to its undoing. A common bird during the 19th Century —with a small russet head and neck, a ruddy breast and long, tapering tail feathers that varied from a slate-blue to an aqua-gray—it ranged chiefly over the eastern half of the United States and the Middle West. Its range also extended to Montana and Texas and east to central Florida. It thrived in such numbers that whole flights would darken the skies. To those who derived a livelihood from killing and marketing wild birds and other game, it was an apparently unending source of prosperity.

Trapped, baited with grain, shot with contrivances that wiped out whole flocks at a time, and sold on the market at all seasons of the year, the passenger pigeon had disappeared from its large population centers by 1850.

In 1870 an even sharper decline in the population was noticed. Still the bird went unprotected, and its slaughter went on unabated. By 1890 the extinction of the passenger pigeon seemed inevitable. It became scarcer and although there occurred a few unconfirmed sightings during the period 1900 to 1907, the last official sighting occurred in September of 1898. The bird had fallen victim to man's greed and his pioneer's belief that the North American wildlife resources were limitless.

The mid-19th to the early 20th Century, more so than any other time in our history, was a period of tragedy for wildlife. It was a time when laws had not yet been enacted to protect rare and threatened species, and a time when the United States was experiencing the great industrial revolution. The exploitation of wildlife continued rapidly with little thought to its protection until some of the early conservationists—John Muir, Theodore Roosevelt, and Gifford Pinchot began their crusading work. In 1883 the American Ornithologists' Union was founded and its members formed a conservation committee whose protective work for endangered species of birds was later taken over by an organization dedicated to conservation—National Association of Audubon Societies founded in 1905 (*See under Egret, and under National Audubon Society*).

The Carolina Parakeet

By the early 1900's, North America and the world, had lost the Carolina parakeet, *Conuropsis carolinensis,* forever from its fauna. The Carolina parakeet was the only member of the parrot family to live northward from the tropics well into the United States. It was approximately the size of a mourning dove, but brilliant in its coloring of bright green and lemon-yellow. Its forehead was marked with orange and red suffusions; its conical tail had long pointed feathers. Ranging from Florida northward to Pennsylvania and New York, westward to North Dakota and Nebraska, and south to Texas, it was shot at by fruit-growers as a nuisance. This double-barreled assault, plus, perhaps, the decimations of disease reduced the Carolina parakeet to a scattered few by 1900. And when its habitat, the heavily forested river valleys and timbered bottomlands of the middle Atlantic, was occupied by settlers, the bird disappeared altogether. The last confirmed sighting was in 1904.

The Eskimo Curlew

As the American pioneers moved to the West across the Great Plains, they discovered huge flights of Eskimo curlews, *Numenius borealis,* moving between their nesting grounds on the coastal tundra of the Arctic and the plains of the Argentine. Unfortunately the bird is not easily distinguished from other curlews so that protection for it was difficult, even after its numbers had diminished. Hunting parties could approach a grounded flock and, almost at their leisure, exterminate every bird without fear of frightening them into flight.

Overshooting, more than any other factor, led to the demise of the Eskimo curlew. The last bird taken in the Great Plains region was in western Nebraska in 1915. One was later shot in 1932 in Newfoundland, the last positive record. However, in 1945 and again, from 1959 to 1964, annual sightings of this supposedly extinct species were made by competent students on Galveston Island, Texas. There is hope, therefore, and a real possibility that the Eskimo curlew went to the very brink of extinction but is now making a comeback.

Other Threatened Species

Some of these are: Attwater's prairie chicken, *Tympanuchus cupido attwateri*, a relative of the now extinct heath hen. The Attwater prairie chicken once inhabited the coastal prairies from northeastern Cameron County, Texas to near Abbeville, Louisiana, but is now limited locally to the coastal area of southeastern Texas. (*See under Chicken: Attwater Prairie Chicken.*)

The ivory-billed woodpecker, *Campephilus principalis*, common in the early 20th Century throughout the heavily wooded areas of the central and southeastern United States, was apparently last seen in 1950 when two of these birds were sighted. There still exists the well-known struggle of the whooping crane, *Grus americana*, to survive (*See under Crane: Whooping Crane*), and the last of a few pairs of the Everglade kite, *Rostrhamus sociabilis*, which were nesting at Lake Okeechobee Florida, up to the spring of 1964. The California condor, *Gymnogyps californianus*, numbering fewer than 50, is now limited to Ventura and Los Angeles counties in southern California (*See under Condor*).

Less in danger, but still requiring protection, are the trumpeter swan, the American flamingo, and the roseate spoonbill. Fortunately, conservationists and naturalists are guarding these birds, and if any one of them becomes extinct, it will be the result of a biological disaster, or the heedlessness of a society that often places emphasis on material wealth at the expense of all other living things.

In the face of this rampant record of extinction, it is somewhat encouraging to note that very few modern species of mammals have been obliterated by man.

This is not to say, however, that the mammal kingdom has not been threatened, for at one time or another, members of almost every group have faced the threat of extinction. Settlers to this continent naturally sought those mammals valuable for fur and food and attacked those they considered predators (*See under Predator*).

Perhaps the most beleaguered North American mammal has been the grizzly bear, *Ursus horribilis*. Weighing as much as 300 or 800 pounds, it is an awesome animal (*See under Bear*). At one time, ten thousand and perhaps many tens of thousands of these magnificent animals ranged from the West Coast to as far inland as the Dakotas and southward through Nebraska, Kansas, Oklahoma, and Texas. But they were pursued relentlessly by hunters, sheepmen, and cattle ranchers, and today the grizzly population in the United States numbers no more than a few hundred. Laws now protect the grizzly, but illegal hunting may in time exterminate this bear from the United States altogether, excepting in protected national parks or wilderness areas.

Like so many other species, the grizzly has been a victim of the occupation of its range by man. As people settled the Pacific coastal valleys and western plains, the grizzlies were killed off, or retreated into more remote wilderness areas.

Fur trapping nearly eliminated the American beaver, *Castor canadensis*, that flat-tailed and ruggedly built dam engineer which initially inhabited nearly every stream and river of the Northeast. After two centuries of heavy trapping by white men and Indians in the United States and Canada it diminished so rapidly that at the turn of the century, it was feared that it would disappear altogether. Fortunately, protective laws were passed to prevent its total extermination and during the last 60 years it has come back strongly (*See under Beaver*).

Overtrapping almost led to the extinction of the fisher, or pekan, *Martes pennanti*. Highly prized for its handsome pelt, this large weasel-like animal weighing from 8 to 18 pounds, was avidly sought after and taken in such numbers that only comparatively few fishers are left in North America. The average annual trappers' catch of fishers in Canada has declined and the animal is gone from many parts of its former range. Fishers are important checks, or controls, on porcupine populations in forested regions—porcupines in large numbers may seriously damage forest trees—(*See Biological Control*). The fisher lives from southeastern Canada and New York state northwest to the Mackenzie River in Canada and south in the Rockies to northeastern Wyoming; and in the Sierras to Sequoia National Park.

The so-called balance of nature is a highly complex oscillation, or rise and fall, of the numbers of animals and the plants they depend upon (*See Balance of Nature*). So interdependent are many animals that the disappearance of one species sometimes pronounces the fate of another. Such is true with the black-footed ferret, *Mustela nigripes,* which occupies the interior plains east of the Rockies and from Texas north to the Dakotas. Its range is practically identical with that of the prairie dog upon which it preys.

In recent years rodent-poisoning campaigns on a large scale have been carried out against the prairie dog on cattle ranges of the West, and it now faces extermination. Many naturalists consider it inevitable that with the extinction of the prairie dog, the black-footed ferret will disappear as well.

The most intensive pressure by man has been put upon the large mammalian predators—the wolves, coyotes, and cougars. Gone from most of its former range is the eastern cougar, or mountain lion,

Labrador ducks

Bison are now protected by the government

Felis concolor. A reddish-brown member of the cat family it grows to a length of 6 feet and weighs up to 175 pounds. As early as the 1690's a bounty was offered for each cougar killed (*See Bounty System*). Today, occasional tracks are reported, and there are indications that the cougar may be coming back where its main prey animal—deer—are increasing (*See under Cats of North America and under Deer*).

The gray wolf, *Canis lupus*, wily and self-sustaining yet hunted as purposefully as any predator, has successfully evaded extinction, although several of the subspecies of the gray wolf, in particular those isolated within a landmass, have disappeared. Such a subspecies is *Canis lupus beothucus*, or the Newfoundland wolf, which followed the caribou herds for food. Readily cornered and killed, it disappeared in numbers about 1900, with the last sighting occurring in 1911.

The red wolf, *Canis niger*, of the southeastern United States is much rarer than the gray wolf and may be on the verge of extinction (*See under Wolves and Foxes of North America*).

Man's assault on the plains bison, *Bison bison*, was the most deliberately destructive of any wild animal in our history. Where once millions freely roamed the interior, now only about 25,000 exist in carefully protected herds either within national parks and monuments or on privately owned preserves. For several centuries the bison provided the Indian with his principle source of food, but with the opening of the West, and in particular the building of the transcontinental railroad, bisons were slaughtered without regard to their survival. The animals were taken for meat and for their hides which were made into robes. So plentiful were they that hunters could afford to pick only the best of those they had shot, leaving the rest to rot in the sun (*See under Bison*).

Man has been slow to act against the threatened extinction of wild animals in the world. As a result we lost forever many of the more helpless creatures of nature. With our loss, however, we acquired knowledge and with our knowledge, an appreciation for our natural heritage. We are no longer ignorant of what man must do to protect that heritage, but we must be wary of indifference. For however knowledgeable we may be, an indifference to the precariously low numbers of the whooping crane, the California condor, the Everglade kite, or the ivory-billed woodpecker, may force upon them the fate of the passenger pigeon, the great auk, the Labrador duck, the Carolina parakeet, and the heath hen.   —J.N.P.

EYESHINE(*See under Poorwill*)

F

FACTS ABOUT BIRDS

There are probably more people interested in birds than in any other group of animals. Many of the accomplishments of birds are well known. Aside from bats birds are the only vertebrates that can truly fly, and a person need only see a bird swoop down from a great height and capture a tiny insect, to realize its keenness of sight. There are many additional accomplishments of birds, however, that are not so familiar to many people.

How Fast Can Birds Fly?

Before the invention of airplanes and stopwatches there was much speculation as to the maximum speed that birds attained in flight. It was thought that birds flew fastest when they were migrating, and some biologists postulated that certain species flew 400 to 500 miles per hour. It was later found from timed flights of birds that these estimated speeds were ridiculously exaggerated.

Data avilable at the present time indicates that certain swifts and falcons are the fastest of the flying birds. Two species of Indian swifts have been timed over a two-mile course and found to average 170 to 200 miles an hour for this distance.

The cloud swifts of the West Indies, which in flight appear and disappear so rapidly, have been estimated to fly at least 150 miles per hour. The European peregrine, often used in falconry, has been timed at a ground speed of 180 miles an hour during a dive, and the duck hawk of the United States has been stated to attain a speed of 165 miles an hour (*See also under Bird: Flight*).

Ostriches and other flightless birds may make up for their inability to fly by their running speed. By actual timing, ostriches have been found to run 50 miles an hour, and they are probably the swiftest of the running birds.

Sizes of Birds

Cock ostriches have been known that were 8 feet high and weighed more than 300 pounds. They are thus the largest of living birds, but the extinct moas of New Zealand were even larger. Relatively complete skeletons of these flightless birds indicate that the largest may have attained a height of 12 feet. A similar group of extinct birds, the elephant birds of Madagascar, may have been heavier, but they were not so tall as the New Zealand moas.

Some hummingbirds are larger than sparrows, but as a group they are the smallest birds in the world. The Cuban bee hummingbird is probably the smallest species. This feathered mite has a body approximately two inches long to which are attached two delicate wings, each of which is one inch in length.

Even some encyclopedias err when discussing the largest wingspread of living birds. Thus figures of 16 to 17 feet may be given for the wingspread of the wandering albatross. Actually, the largest wingspread of an albatross ever measured was 11 feet, 4 inches. This is probably the greatest wingspread of any living bird, although some people believe that the South American condor is even larger. Robert Cushman Murphy of the American Museum of Natural History measured the wingspread of a condor shot off the coast of South America and found it to be slightly more than 10 feet. This is the largest authentic measurement so far taken of one of these birds.

The wingspread of another North American bird, the trumpeter swan, is about the same as that of the condors. Biologists measured one individual that had a wingspread of 10 feet, 2 inches.

The Proportions of Birds

For the smallest wings in proportion to body size, the kiwi, a flightless New Zealand bird about the size of a chicken, will almost certainly rank first. Its wings are so reduced that they cannot be seen unless one pushes the body feathers aside. Once this is done, small fingerlike stubs representing the wings can be

found. These feeble structures are, of course, no more useful to the kiwi than appendixes are to human beings.

The hummingbirds are noted for their smallness, but in proportion of length of beak to body size, one species probably exceeds all other birds. This is a South American form, appropriately called the swordbill. These birds, which obtain nectar and small insects from long tubular flowers, have beaks approximately five inches long. One might even say that the beak "wags the bird" since it is longer than the remainder of its body (See Adaptations of Birds).

The records for the largest sizes of beaks, proportionate to body size, are held by some of the hornbills and toucans. The massive beaks of these birds are supposed to assist them in reaching for fruit upon which many of them feed. Most of these beaks are hollow, and thus are not so heavy as they appear, but in some African hornbills they are solid. This fact has contributed to the destruction of these birds because natives use their beaks for carving love charms. As a consequence, hornbills are relatively rare in many areas.

The Sizes of Birds' Eggs

All birds lay eggs. Most birds incubate their eggs with the heat from their bodies. Even though all eggs are quite similar in structure, their range in size is truly amazing. Some hummingbirds lay eggs that are barely a quarter of an inch long, while the ostrich produces eggs that weigh several pounds and may be six or seven inches long. Such an egg has a bulk equal to more than a dozen hens' eggs. A single ostrich egg could take care of the breakfast requirements of a rather large family.

The eggs of ostriches seem large compared with those of most living birds, but they are small compared with those of the extinct elephant birds of Madagascar. Almost complete shells of these giant eggs have been discovered. They are large enough to hold more than two gallons of liquid, six times the capacity of an ostrich egg.

The kiwi of New Zealand lays the largest egg, in proportion to its body size, of any known vertebrate animal. A kiwi weighs about four pounds; one of its eggs may weigh a pound and be five inches long.

The incubation period of a hen's egg is about 21 days. As a rule, the larger the egg, the longer the incubation period, but the length of incubation is not always proportionate to the egg size. For example, hummingbirds' eggs, the smallest known, require about 16 days to hatch, yet some sparrows' eggs, which are larger, require only 12 to 13 days.

The cowbird lays its eggs in the nests of other birds (*See under Cowbird*).

The eggs of the cowbird have an incubation period of 11 to 12 days, occasionally 13, and even 14 days. Often a cowbird egg hatches before those laid by the rightful owner of the nest. The cowbird, being older than the other youngsters, can more than hold its own in competition for food, and it may even push the smaller birds from the nest.

As might be expected, the longest incubation periods are found among the larger birds. Surprisingly, the ostrich egg hatches in a shorter time than those of some of its smaller cousins. The ostrich egg takes only about 42 days compared with approximately 60 days required for cassowary and emu eggs (*See also under Bird: Birds' Nests*).

How Long Do Birds Live?

The potential length of life of birds has probably been exaggerated more than any other fact about them. Swans, birds of prey, and parrots are the most famous of these alleged Methuselahs. Reported ages of captive birds include an eagle of 104, a vulture of 118, and a parrot of 120. Biologists who have investigated this matter in recent times have failed to produce a single centenarian among birds. It is admitted that some might live longer than modern authentic rec-

ords indicate, but all such reported extreme ages must be regarded with suspicion until they are verified. Reasonably well-established ages of captive birds include an owl of 68, an eagle of 55, a condor of 52, and a pelican of 51.

Some of the smaller birds live for a surprisingly long time. Records of a cardinal of 30, a house sparrow of 23, and a canary of 22 all seem reasonably well established, although all of these were caged birds. (*See also under Bird*)

—O.P.B.

FALCON

Falcons are hawks classified in a special group (*See also Buteo*). They are slender, streamlined birds of the family Falconidae with long, pointed wings, and notched bills. All are exceptionally fast fliers, and one, the peregrine falcon, *Falco peregrinus*, has been clocked at 175 miles an hour in its swoop or power dive (*See under Facts About Birds*).

The gyrfalcon, *Falco rusticolus*, is the largest of the family. A handsome bird of the Arctic, it has a variable plumage. Some individuals are pure white with flecks of black on the back and wings; others have more and more black coloring until the other extreme is reached— all black except for white streaking on the underparts. Arctic hares and lemmings are the main items of its diet in most regions, but when these animals are scarce the gyrfalcons take gulls, ducks, and murres. Severe winters bring a few gyrfalcons southward into the United States.

The peregrine falcon, *Falco peregrinus*, also called the duck hawk, is the size of the common crow, about 19 inches long. It is slate-blue above, streaked and barred below, with a distinctive black cap and black "mustachial" face markings. Birds are its chief food; plovers and terns are taken by peregrine falcons living along the coast, birds of jay- and robin-size by those dwelling in the country, and semidomestic pigeons by those that visit the cities. The prey is usually struck from above, after a swift dive, and is killed by a blow from the falcon's powerful feet and raking talons. The peregrine may catch its prey in the air, if it is small enough, or, with a larger bird, it may follow it down after striking it out of the air, and feed upon it where it lands. Smaller birds are sometimes plucked from the air with one talon.

Peregrines require a wide hunting range and guard their territories jealously. They were never very common in the eastern United States, and they no longer breed there. The most probable cause, in these days when hawks are protected everywhere from hunting, is the too-liberal use of pesticides for insect control (*See under Insecticide and under Pesticide*).

The open range of the West, from Alberta to Mexico, is the home of the prairie falcon, *Falco mexicanus*. It has about the same measurements as the peregrine, but is lighter in weight and in color and without the black cap. The top of the head is the same light brown as the back; each dark eye is larger proportionately than a peregrine's, has a white line over it, and from it a brown line descends to cross the white cheek. In flight the prairie falcon shows a dusky patch under each wing at the body line. It hunts at a lower level than the peregrine, cruising above the ground at less than 50 feet. It swoops down occasionally at birds of grouse-size and less, but is a more regular feeder on mammals such as the prairie dog and ground squirrels. The nest is a bare, "scrape" usually in a natural cavity in the rock, often near the top of a cliff and bare of nesting materials.

The pigeon hawk, *Falco columbarius*, is a dove-sized falcon, and strikingly like a miniature peregrine falcon. It is dark on the back, with interrupted streaking on the underside. With an inconspicuous dark cap and no facial patterning, its most distinctive feature is the heavily barred tail with the widest band near the tip. The pigeon hawk subsists largely on small birds and large insects such as dragonflies (*See Dragonfly*). The breeding range coincides with the spruce and fir forests of the northern hemisphere, and the wintering range encompasses the United States and northern South America.

The smallest falcon in North America is called the sparrow hawk, *Falco sparverius*. The English name of kestrel is more suitable than sparrow hawk, which implies that this insect-eater preys solely on the smaller sparrow. In winter however, it does take mice and birds as large as a cardinal.

The male sparrow hawk is the most colorful of the North American falcons; it has a chestnut cap with a gray border; back and tail are chestnut; the wings are blue-gray; and there are two black bars and one black spot on each side of the face and neck. The female and the young birds are less colorful than the male, but back and tail are marked black and brown, and the same facial markings are present. This little falcon is a breeding bird throughout most of the continent, and its hovering flight and nearly constant *kli-kli-kli* call are everywhere familiar to people who are aware of birds.

The Sport of Falconry

In Asia, beginning at least by 2000 B.C., and later in Europe, falcons were trained to hunt. Falconry was a sport of the nobility, and in many lands a man's social status determined which hawk he might own. Possession of a gyrfalcon was, in Europe, the prerogative of the nobility. Falconry became both a highly developed art and an impressive ritual with a vocabulary and a code of its own.

Falconry was also a means of hunting for food. Young hawks were taken from the nest, or adults were caught while "in passage" (migration). In the field the bird is carried on the falconer's fist, held by a leather jesse attached to each

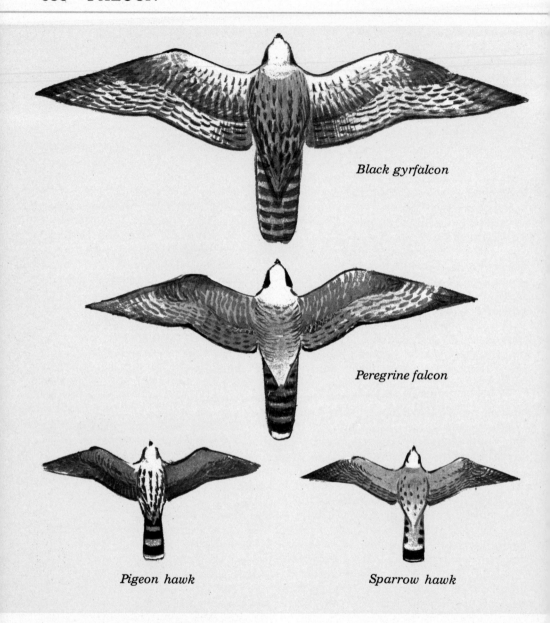

Black gyrfalcon

Peregrine falcon

Pigeon hawk

Sparrow hawk

leg, and a leather leash which the falconer detaches when releasing his falcon at wild quarry.

While carrying the bird, it is kept hooded to prevent it from seeing other game until the falconer is ready to release it at the chosen quarry. Once the falcon has struck and killed the crow, pigeon, or other winged prey, the falconer walks cautiously to the falcon,

helps it to feed from its quarry, and thus retrieves his bird.

Large birds, such as the herons and the bustard, were the favorite targets in Europe and Asia. In Persia large hawks and eagles were used in falconry to bring down gazelles. In recent times, falconers in Central Asia have used golden eagles to hunt foxes and even wolves.

—G.B.S.

Adult peregrine falcon (immature,in flight)

Peregrine Falcon
Other Common Names—Duck hawk, peregrine
Scientific Name—*Falco peregrinus*
Family—Falconidae (caracaras and falcons)
Order—Falconiformes
Size—Length, 17 to 19 inches
Range—From Alaska and Greenland south through North America, Mexico, Central America, to the tip of South America. In the Old World from northern Scandanavia, Russia, Siberia, south through Europe, Asia, Africa, and Southeast Asia to Australia and Tasmania. Not found on the islands of the eastern Pacific nor in New Zealand

Adult male prairie falcon

Prairie Falcon
Other Common Names—Mountain hawk
Scientific Name—*Falco mexicanus*
Family—Falconidae (caracaras and falcons)
Order—Falconiformes

Size—Length, 17½ to 19½ inches
Range—Nests from central British Columbia, southern Alberta and Saskatchewan, and North Dakota south to Baja California, southern Arizona, New Mexico, and northern Texas

Adult black gyrfalcon (immature, in flight)

Black Gyrfalcon
Other Common Names—None
Scientific Name—*Falco rusticolus obsoletus*
Family—Falconidae (caracaras and falcons)
Order—Falconiformes

Size—Length, 22 inches
Range—Breeds from Victoria Island, Devon Island, Ellesmere Island, and Greenland, south to northern Quebec, northern Labrador, and Southhampton Island. Winters largely in far North but occasionally in northern United States

Adult white gyrfalcon (immature, in flight)

White Gyrfalcon
Other Common Names—White hawk, white falcon
Scientific Name—*Falco rusticolus candicans*
Family—Falconidae (caracaras and falcons)

Order—Falconiformes
Size—Length, 22 inches
Range—Eastern Arctic, North America, and Greenland. South in winter to British Columbia, Montana, Ontario, Quebec, and Maine

Pigeon hawks (male, perched; female, in flight)

Pigeon Hawk
Other Common Names—Merlin, bullet hawk
Scientific Name— *Falco columbarius*
Family—Falconidae (caracaras and falcons)
Order—Falconiformes
Size—Length, 10 to 13 inches
Range—From northern Alaska, Mackenzie, Manitoba, Quebec, and Labrador to British Columbia, North Dakota, Michigan, and Nova Scotia. South in winter to Peru and Venezuela, the West Indies, and Trinidad. In Old World; Iceland, Scandinavia, and Siberia, south in winter to northern Africa and India, southern China and Japan

Immature male sparrow hawk

After banding, this young sparrow hawk will be released

Sparrow Hawk
Other Common Names— Killy hawk, American kestrel
Scientific Name— *Falco sparverius*
Family— Falconidae (caracaras and falcons)
Order— Falconiformes

Size— Length, 9½ to 11 inches
Range— Northern Alaska and northwestern Canada, southern Quebec and Nova Scotia, south through the Americas (including the West Indies) to Argentina and Tierra del Fuego

FALSE SOLOMON'S SEAL

Other Common Names—False spikenard, Solomon's zigzag, Solomon's plumes
Scientific Name— *Smilacina racemosa*
Family—Liliaceae (lily family)
Range—Quebec to British Columbia, south to Nova Scotia, New England, Virginia, upland of North Carolina and Tennessee, Missouri, and other states
Habitat—Woods, clearings, and bluffs
Time of Blooming—Mid-May through July

In early summer the compact clusters of tiny, six-petaled, six-stamened, white flowers growing on the tip of a nodding stem add grace and interest to the parade of blooming plants. The stem, sometimes zigzagged, may have eight or more leaves arranged alternately and slightly folded lengthwise.

The name for this plant, false Solomon's seal, no doubt refers to the fact that the "seal," which is left in the autumn when the upper portion dies back to the root, is not such a perfect replica of the old seals as that of the "true" Solomon's seal, *Polygonum biflorum*. The flowers of the latter are yellow and hang from the axils of the leaves on slender stems. The berries of the latter are a deep blue while those of the false Solomon's seal are first green, then red, spotted with magenta; in the late summer they become almost a translucent red. They can often be seen clinging to the dead stem, well into the winter season.

The berries of the five species of *Smilacina* present in the woodlands of the United States are eaten by wildlife, including the ruffed grouse, the band-tailed pigeon, and gray-cheeked and olive-backed thrushes, the veery, the white-footed mouse, and the wood rat.

The plant is gathered in large quantities by florists who use them for the greenery in their bouquets or sell them as one of their cut flowers; however, the false Solomon's seal is on the conservation lists of many states, which means

False Solomon's seal

that in some locations they should not be picked.

FASCICLE (*See under Pine*)

FEATHER

The reptilian ancestors of birds were clothed in a leathery skin that was studded with scales. These surface projections were composed of a horny protein called *keratin*. As the evolutionary process continued, succeeding generations of creatures, which were part bird and part reptile, developed scales that were increasingly longer and divided. Eventually, these scales became feathers—structures that are far more complex and with entirely different functions than scales but of the same chemical composition (*See under Bird*). Scales served merely to protect the skin of cold-blooded animals; feathers provide a means of heat insulation for the warm-blooded birds, and also give them lightness in their winged flight (*See under Bird: Flight*).
—G.B.S.

Blue jay feathers appear blue because of boxlike surface cells

Colors of Feathers

Next to the magic of winged flight, no feature of birds brings greater pleasure than the variety and beauty of their plumage colors and patterns. Color patterns are also the means by which people can most readily distinguish most of the species and the sexes of many of them.

It is natural to wonder what particular ingredients or internal processes give the scarlet tanager his flame, the crow his somber coat, or combine to paint the whole range of the colors of birds' feathers—from russet or yellow or green to violet or gray or white.

Research on animal coloration has been carried far by many investigators in the United States and abroad. Among the earlier efforts were Krukenberg's analysis in the 1880's of the feather colors of flamingos, birds of paradise, finches, and woodpeckers, and Mayer's work on feather surface structures, near the turn of the century.

In recent decades great progress has been made in improving the techniques necessary to sift and identify complex organic pigments, and to break down ultramicroscopic cellular arrangements in bird feather surfaces. Pigmentation and surface structure are, in fact, the two basic factors that underlie the coloration of birds—and, for that matter, of hair, skin, carapace, and tissue throughout the animal world, from protozoa to mankind.

An exploration into the technicalities of color will lead from elementary optics and chemistry into the diversity of coaltar dyes, snowflakes, sky color, a film of oil on a wet asphalt pavement, the splendor of a wood duck's iridescence, and the differences between molecules that set the yellow-shafted flicker apart from the red-shafted—and from their orange hybrids. Even the phosphorescent eye-shine of nocturnal animals caught in our headlights is part of this vast area of research.

What is Color?

It is pertinent here to recall that color is the physical phenomenon by which a given object absorbs most of the visible wavelengths of a light except those in and near a specific color band in the spectrum. The unabsorbed wavelengths are then reflected to the eye. A pure black object absorbs all visible wavelengths. Grays fall between the two by partial absorption of the whole spectrum.

All feather colors result from either —or both—the physical structure of the feather's surface, and the specific chemical nature of pigments contained inside its shaft, barb or barbule, or the microscopic hooklets that bind the barbules together. Thus, a blue jay's "blue" comes from a surface structure of boxlike cells overlying a black or gray inner pigment that reflects light back through the thin, hornlike surface-sheath in blue wavelengths. There is no blue pigment in a blue jay's feathers.

By contrast, the orange fire of an oriole is due solely to pigments in the feathers, whereas the white of a whistling swan—or of an arctic fox—is en-

The feathers of birds are colored by complex pigments and the arrangement of surface cells that reflect certain wavelengths of the color spectrum

tirely the result of light of all visible wavelengths being thrown back from colorless cells in and beneath the surface of feather or hair.

There are three major types of feather structural colors. These are the whites of total reflection displayed by the swan; the Tyndall blues of scattered reflection, exemplified by the blue feathers of a bluebird, jay, or macaw; and the iridescent jewels worn by many pheasants, waterfowl, hummingbirds, and blackbirds—from crows to grackles.

Iridescence

It is worth noting that an iridescent feather changes "color" as the angle from which it is seen shifts, whereas a white or blue feather keeps its color whatever the angle it is viewed from, darkening only as the intensity of light thrown upon it decreases. Iridescence is the product of light waves striking through successive and very thin films of colorless surface cells to an inner brown, gray, or black pigment, which then reflects back to the eye as colors from different parts of the spectrum.

Pigment Groups

Most of the plumage colors of nearly all North American birds are derived largely from pigments, and most of these fall into two major groups—the *carotenoids* and the *melanins*. Carotenoids are double-bonded hydrocarbons and related compounds bearing some oxygen atoms, not very different from many of the coal-tar dyes of industry. Melanins are more complex organic compounds, produced by protein catabolism, and carry nitrogen, sulphur, oxygen, and, in some cases, iron or other metal atoms as well.

Carotenoids are the most widely distributed conspicuous pigments found in nature. They are present in nearly all animals from the lowest to the highest forms, and in all plants from fungi to highly organized seed-bearers. Animals obtain them directly by ingestion of plant food or by predation on other animals.

The carotenoid pigments are responsible for many brilliant feather colors, from red, yellow, and orange to bright brown and, in combination with certain proteins or surface structures, even green and purple. They, in turn, are divided into several chemical categories, such as the carotenes and the oxygen-carrying carotene derivatives, the latter including the xanthophylls, a frequent source of yellow in feathers. Metal salts and oxides play little part in the color of most bird feathers. Plumage colors thus resemble those of synthetic dyes and differ from the inorganic pigments found in paints and enamels.

Melanins are part of the *indole* pigment group, resulting from the grouping of oxidized products of one of three colorless amino acids. They are manufactured within the animal, unlike the ingested carotenoids. Melanins are the pigments that produce most of the black, gray, brown, tawny, and some yellow animal hair and feather colors, as well as cuttlefish ink, and human suntan. The colors of ravens, crows, and blackbirds represent the most lavish, concentrated displays of melanin found among birds. When screened by surface laminations, melanins also result in marvelous iridescent plumages and insect scales.

There are several other types of pigments in the living world, all of them organic in composition. Most of them, however, give color to plants, to other animals, to egg yolk, blood, tissues, or skin, rather than to feathers. These pigments comprise such groups as the chromolipoids, quinones, anthocyans and flavones, tetraphyrroles, flavins, purines, and pterins.

One of the tetraphyrroles, a porphyrin known as turacin, is responsible for giving the fruit-eating African touracos their vivid red underwing plumage, while an oxidized derivative of the same pigment is responsible for the green feathers worn by variants of the same birds.

Although green feathers are displayed by very few North American bird species, they provide interesting material for future laboratory investigation. In the parrot tribe, green plumage is usually the by-product of a microscopic surface structure over black or gray melanin, such as would normally yield a "blue" wavelength. Instead, a yellow xanthophyll carotenoid also enters within the barbules, converting the blue to green. A striking result of the alliance of two different classes of pigments and diverse surface arrangements is the remarkable number of feather color mutations shown by the domesticated Australian shell parakeet, *Melopsicattus undulatus,* which has outdistanced the canary as America's most popular cagebird.

Parakeet Colors

In its original wild plumage, the parakeet has a green breast and rump, yellow throat and forehead, deep blue tail, and scalelike pattern of black and yellow on wings and back. But now, barely more than a century since these birds were first imported into England, their color variations run into something over 1,300 recognized common types, from albino, ice-blue and sky-blue, to yellow, cobalt, and deep violet, all shades of green from deep olive to pale apple, and scores of rarer grays, opalines, mauves, and cinnamons. No other bird species has shown such versatility in combining the triple possibilities of melanins, carotenoids, and structural colors, and thereby exhibiting hues at nearly all the possible points of the chromatic compass.

Analyzing Color Pigments

A procedure for analyzing the pigments in bird feathers has been developed by Frederick H. Test, of the University of Michigan, to determine the nature of the red, yellow, and orange pigments of flickers. It is a delicate, exacting, and complicated operation that begins with the maceration and pulverization of carefully selected feathers of the color to be

Carolina parakeets from Audubon's Elephant Folio

analyzed. The powdered material is first subjected to various solvents. In the case of carotenoids, the carotenes can be segregated from the xanthophylls by injecting the dissolved pigment into a glass tube in which there are two immiscible solvents — a light ether floating above a heavier alcohol. Any carotenes rise into the upper, "epiphasic" hydrocarbon layer, while the xanophylls are drawn down into the "hypophasic" alcohol. This is only a preliminary stage, which is easily upset if the solvents are shaken together.

A subsequent step takes the respective pigments through a glass cylinder packed with a powdered alkali, such as calcium carbonate, to which the various different types of carotenoids adhere at different levels, in chromatographic array. The difficulty of the technique is increased by the fact that the entire catalogue of all the possible carotenes and xanthophylls has not yet been compiled and knowledge of their molecular structures and their differing reactions to solvents, mineral acids, and other agents is unknown.

Thus, according to Frederick H. Test, the cardinal's red pigment resists extraction by the ordinary carotene solvents, and may belong to some other group of pigments. A flamingo's pink, on the other hand, dissolves quickly in wood or grain alcohol, and is so sensitive to the bird's diet that captive birds rapidly fade into white if deprived of shrimp and other carotenoid-rich fare. Canaries also turn white, at the molt, if kept on a carotenoid-free diet, whereas parakeets retain their yellow color on such rations (*See under Animal: Colors of Animals*).

Under such difficulties it is not surprising that, so far only a few colors of bird feather pigments and structural surfaces of only a small number of bird species have been analyzed. Even so, enough is already known to state the basic principles and to invite deeper and wider investigations. It is obvious that painstaking work by many men would be needed to determine even the surface and pigmental factors that distinguish only the gorget colors of the fewer than 20 hummingbird species that occur north of the Mexican border.

Sexual Dichromatism

An arresting aspect of sexual dichromatism in birds is the different metabolism between the sexes in turkeys and peacocks (*See Dichromatism under Animal: Colors of Animals*). In both species, the males secrete much larger amounts of protein in the form of feather keratins than do their mates, whose protein intake is needed primarily for egg production. Moreover, the males differ from the hens in the manner in which such proteins are deposited in multilayered, thin films over the melanin-laden barbules of their feathers, producing richly beautiful iridescent colors. Perhaps some similar sex differences in metabolism will be found accountable for the brighter colors worn by the males in many other families of birds. —G.D.

Ferns resemble seed plants in having roots, stems, and leaflike fronds. Reproduction, however, is by spores

Unopened fiddleheads of cinnamon ferns push up through the forest floor

FERNS

Ferns and their relatives belong to a very ancient group of plants whose ancestry dates back many millions of years. They reached their greatest size and numbers during the Carboniferous Period some 200 million years ago. The imprints in coal of these ferns of long ago give us a clue to their relationship to some of the ferns of today. The tree ferns of the tropical regions are directly descended from the ancient species. Our so-called "flowering ferns," the royal, interrupted, and cinnamon ferns, also are close relatives of ancient ferns of the coal period. Other fern fossils resemble the forms of our present-day maidenhair and bracken ferns.

Today ferns live throughout the world except in arctic and severe desert regions. They are most numerous in hot, moist areas. About 250 species of ferns grow in North America north of Mexico and it is estimated that there are about 6,000 described species in the world. Thirty-five species of ferns found in one region at 40° north are a very rich fern population for temperate North America.

Although ferns produce no flowers their plumosely divided leaves (fronds) add beauty and grace to forests, cliffs, swamps, hillsides, and other damp places. They are of great importance as pioneers in soil-building as they can survive where more highly organized plants cannot. Very probably the role of ferns as soil builders has been of even greater importance to mankind than the part their substances played in the production of coal.

Some ferns grow on tops of rocks or in crevices where very little soil has accumulated. The common polypody, *Polypodium vulgare,* is a good example of a fern that thrives on the tops of ledges, while the small species of spleenworts typify those that grow in crevices of rocks or high on cliff sides. Decayed material from their dead fronds adds humus to the soil and makes possible the later growth of larger plants that

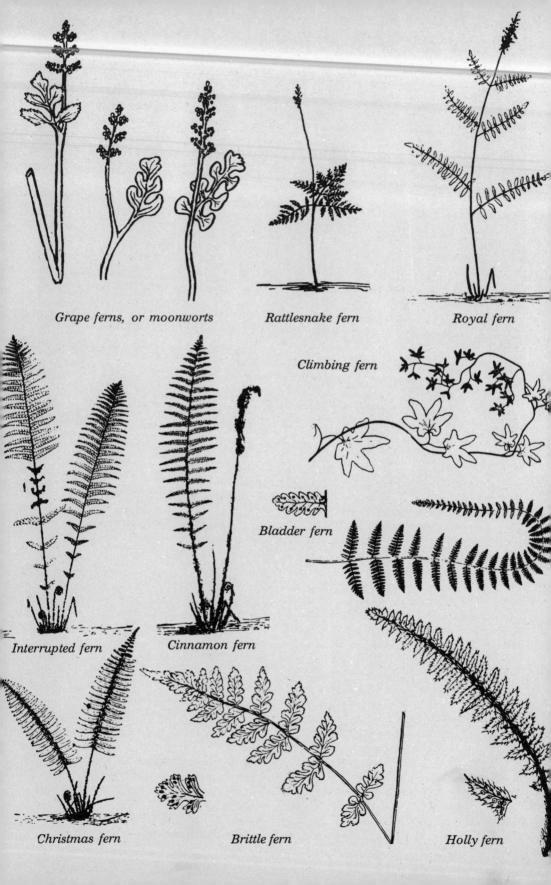

Grape ferns, or moonworts

Rattlesnake fern

Royal fern

Climbing fern

Interrupted fern

Cinnamon fern

Bladder fern

Christmas fern

Brittle fern

Holly fern

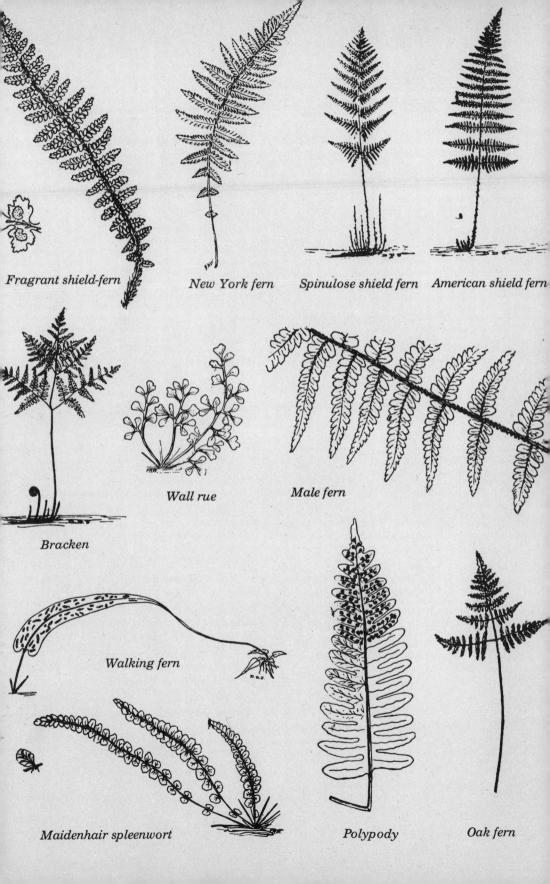

Fragrant shield-fern   *New York fern*   *Spinulose shield fern*   *American shield fern*

Wall rue   *Male fern*

Bracken

Walking fern

Maidenhair spleenwort   *Polypody*   *Oak fern*

must have deeper soil in which to live. Plants such as algae, mosses, and lichens usually precede ferns in this plant succession that may begin in places barren of soil.

How Ferns Reproduce

How ferns get a start in crevices of rocks or on cliffs and other high places can best be understood if something of the life history of these spore-producing plants is understood. Ferns do not reproduce their kind by means of seeds as the flowering plants do, but are dependent on microscopic-size spores. Since these spores are so small, and light, they are carried by the wind into many inaccessible places.

Seeds grow into plants similar to the parent, but when a spore is planted it must pass through two stages before doing so. From the spore a tiny flat *thallus,* about one-fourth of an inch across, will develop. This is called a prothallium. Upon its underside will appear two sets of cells, the male and female cells. If there is sufficient moisture surrounding the prothallium the male cell can float to the female cell. From this union will develop the familiar fern plant. Green spots (they turn brown when ripe) on the back of fern fronds are the groups of minute pouches (*sporangia*) in which the spores of the fern grow. There are many of these pouches in each spot (a *sorus*) and probably hundreds of spores in each pouch. If you wish to see a fern prothallium, look in a forest beneath the upturned roots of trees or an undercut of a shaded bank where there is constant water seepage. If you find a number of tiny fern plants you will be quite likely to find the minute prothallia among them. Late July and August are the best months to look for them if you live in the northern states.

Growing Ferns Indoors

Prothallia can be grown without much difficulty from the spores of the royal fern, *Osmunda regalis.* They should be collected while the spore cases are open

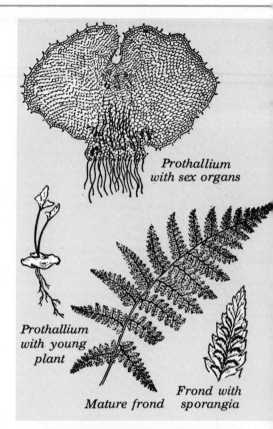

Prothallium with sex organs

Prothallium with young plant

Mature frond

Frond with sporangia

Reproduction of ferns (see text)

but still yellow-green in color. Dust the spores onto a piece of damp blotting paper. Set the blotting paper on edge in a dish of water so the blotter can absorb a constant supply of water. Place an upturned glass over the dish and keep in a warm room. It must have light but not direct sunlight. It will take about three weeks or more for the spores to grow into prothallia and several more days before the first tiny frond will appear from beneath the prothallium. If you have even a hand lens of four-power magnification it will be a help in observing the growth of the new fern from the prothallium.

Fiddleheads and Crosiers

Fern fronds are rolled up like a watch spring when they come through the ground, and slowly uncoil. These coiled

Bulblet fern

Walking fern

Christmas fern

Bracken fern

fronds are commonly called crosiers, or fiddleheads. The latter name is derived from their similarity to the head of a violin. Or it might be more proper to say that the head of the violin is a decorative use we make of this fern characteristic. Many people use the crosiers of the bracken, interrupted, cinnamon, and other ferns in salads or as a cooked vegetable. Cinnamon ferns are covered with a thick coat of wooly substance that humans discard before eating the crosier, but the ruby-throated hummingbird uses the plant wool to line its nest.

Some Common Ferns of North America

Those who travel in Europe find many familiar ferns, as many of their ferns are the same as ours. The *bracken, royal, fragile, male, beech, wall rue, maidenhair spleenwort, hart's tongue, holly fern,* and others grow both in Europe and in the northern United States. In fact, more of the eastern United States ferns may be found by traveling to England than by searching in areas west of the Rocky Mountains. However, such ferns as the beech, male, oak, maidenhair spleenwort, lady, and a few others, grow in both eastern and western parts of the United States. The bracken fern (*Pteridium*) in some of its forms, grows from coast to coast and from Canada to Mexico. The Christmas fern, *Polystichum acrostichoides,* of the East, has a close relative on the West Coast in the sword fern, *Polystichum munitum.* The sword fern is very similar in appearance to the Christmas fern but grows much larger. It is abundant from Alaska to central California.

Some Uses of Ferns

Our shield ferns, American shield fern, *Dryopteris intermedia,* and spinulose shield fern, *Dyropteris spinulosa,* and others, are known in England as buckler ferns. In the United States the American and spinulose shield ferns are collected by the tons during the late summer and put into cold storage to be used later

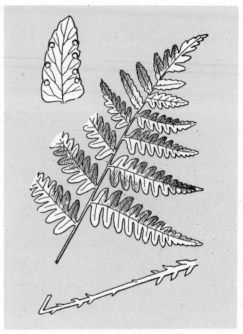

Marginal shield fern

by florists. When collecting the ferns, if care is taken not to loosen them from their rooted moorings no harm is done to the plant because the fronds have finished their season's growth and their production of spores.

No doubt the familiar Boston fern, so called because it was near Boston that a number of varieties were developed, has become the most important in the commercial world. The parent of the Boston fern is the sword fern, *Nephrolepis exaltata,* whose native home is in the Everglades of Florida and the West Indies. The sword fern was not developed from the Christmas fern as so many people surmise.

Cultivation and Development of Ferns

The sword fern was first introduced into cultivation in North America about 1793. Since that time more than 200 distinct forms have been developed and about one hundred have been given names. The many forms of this fern were started from the runners that grow at the base of the plant and will attach

Ebony spleenwort

themselves to the ground at the end of the runner and grow a new plant like the parent. Occasionally, this new plant will be more finely cut or vary from the parent plant enough to propagate it for its varied form. These variations have been the source of the hundreds of the cut-leaved forms of the Boston fern. This form of reproduction is known as vegetative and is usually not as hazardous as reproduction by means of spores.

The walking fern, *Camptosaurus rhizophyllus,* "walks" by taking root at the tips of the fronds where their tips come in contact with the ground. The bladder, or bulblet, fern, *Crystopteris bulbifera,* produces bulblets at the axils of the veins that grow directly into new plants like the parent. Very few of our ferns are capable of reproducing themselves by means of vegetative multiplication except by root rhizomes.

The rhizomes of royal, cinnamon, and interrupted ferns are quite large and the bases of the fronds adhere to the rhizome for many years. These rough rhizomes make a fine media upon which horticulturists raise the epyphitic (*See Epiphyte*) orchids (those that do not require soil in which to grow).

Other Uses of Ferns

In Siam, baskets are woven from the stems of a climbing fern and in other countries the dark mahogany-colored stems of maidenhair are used for the same purpose.

In Siberia the Yakuts make a tea from the fragrant fern. In the United States the fragrant fern grows only on cliffs in scattered northern areas. It is so viscid that the fronds adhere one to the other when crushed. In colonial times this fern was used as a sachet.

The rootstalk of the licorice fern, *Polypodium glycirhiza,* of the West Coast is eaten by some as a delicacy. It is a close relative of the common polypody of the eastern United States.

In the tropics the trunks of tree ferns, because of their durability and the fact that termites do not live in their wood, are used as building timbers. Many of the tropical species of ferns are sold as houseplants.

Plants Mistaken for Ferns

Because some of the flowering plants have plumosely divided leaves like those of the ferns, they are often mistaken for them, especially when these plants are small, usually in their winter rosette stage. Such plants as wild carrot, or Queen Ann's lace, *Daucus carota,* sweet fern, *Comptonia peregrina,* wood betony, *Pedicularis canadensis,* yarrow, *Achillea millefolium,* and asparagus fern, *Asparagus plumosa,* a relative of the asparagus, are all commonly mistaken for ferns.

In olden days ferns, because there was lack of knowledge about how ferns reproduce, were credited with strange powers. Some of these superstitions have been recorded in myths and folklore. One superstition about the moonworts, or grape ferns, was that if any one carried a "seed" of these ferns in his pocket he could become invisible at will. Willard N. Clute in his book, *Our Ferns,* cites many of these old ideas about ferns. —F.A.W.

Recommended Reading

The Fern Allies of North America North of Mexico—Willard Nelson Clute. Frederick A. Stokes & Company, New York.
Fern Guide—Edgar T. Wherry. Doubleday & Company, Inc., Garden City, New York.

FIELD TRIP

Field trips are not only essential and fascinating to the professional scientist, but they also are necessary and inspirational to the interested amateur. For the scientist, work in the field gives him a knowledge of a living organism in its natural surroundings and its relationship to other animals or plants. The scientist also makes field trips to collect insects, mammals, birds, plants, rocks, and other material in which he may be interested, which he then can study more closely in the laboratories.

People can learn many things about nature from field trips or nature walks. The many mysteries of life can be observed firsthand. For example—field trips may be scheduled to take advantage of some seasonal feature such as the migration or roosting of birds, the blooming of spring wild flowers, autumn coloration of leaves, or to study wildlife in winter (*See under Winter*). Other trips may be timed to observe less familiar natural phenomena: to watch the spring migration of frogs, toads, and salamanders and to find their egg masses in rain-filled ponds, to observe hawk migration from some high ridge; to explore a cave and find hibernating bats; to visit a trout hatchery, a forest tree nursery, or some other demonstration of wildlife conservation in action.

The many worthwhile objectives of field trips include: (1) the excitement that comes from experiencing the sights and sounds of nature, even the taste, smell, and feel of it; (2) the satisfaction derived from discovering the interdependence of living things, the relationship of cause and effect in nature, and the predictable events in the recurring cycle of the seasons; (3) a deeper respect for living things, good outdoor manners, and an understanding of the role of local, state, and national conservation agencies and organizations; (5) a sound basis for developing a lifelong interest in the out-of-doors, for wholesome use of leisure time, and for appreciating the value and need of conservation.

Field trips or nature walks are becoming increasingly more popular. In New England, John Brainerd runs "landscape analysis trips" to see "what the Lord and Man have done—to see what we like and what we don't like." Using a public address system and traveling in caravans or by bus, Brainerd also conducts "Oh my! Tours," to see and photograph autumn coloration and discover some of the meaningful biological facts of that season.

An increasing number of nature centers are being established, with a variety of methods used to interpret, identify, or to explain the phenomena of nature. One would find it worthwhile to see how classes of school children and adult groups are introduced to the mysteries of nature. Audubon Centers are located at Greenwich and Sharon, Connecticut, Dayton, Ohio, and El Monte (near Los Angeles), California; sanctuaries of state Audubon societies are in Massachusetts, Rhode Island, New Jersey, and Florida; the Little Red School House and other nature centers are in the Forest Preserve of Cook County, Illinois; the Rock Creek Nature Center, in Washington, D.C.; and Antioch College's Glen Helen Nature Center, Yellow Springs, Ohio. Generally an interested visitor can arrange to accompany a scheduled group if he writes (or phones) ahead.

The United States Forest Service has organized very successful "Show Me Tours,"—caravans that visit areas where forest conservation problems and practices may be observed. Nationwide Interpretive service was inaugurated in 1961.

By far the largest and most expert corps of nature guides are the ranger-naturalists of the United States National Park Service. Though the year-round personnel are few in number, several hundred seasonal men and women are employed. Some have been engaged tor

Geological field trip in Grand Canyon

Shell hunting on the Atlantic Coast

a three-month period every summer for ten to twenty years or more. Through rich experiences and a fine in-service training program, they have become an inspiring team of interpreters of the natural world and convincing exponents of the conservation of our natural resources. —C.E.M.

Audubon Nature Bulletins: *Wildlife Preserves of Schools, Camps and Communities; Trees Are History Books; How to Build a Nature Trail;* and others will be especially helpful to persons responsible for organizing or conducting trips.

Field Book Of Nature Activities—William Hilcourt, G. P. Putnam's Sons, New York.

A house finch can improvise a nest from a variety of materials

FINCH

The name finch is usually applied to any of the seedeaters, those many species of small birds with short, stout, conical bills. Their chief food is seeds, usually those encased in hard, waxy hulls.

The finches comprise two very similar families, the Fringillidae, or New World seedeaters, and the Ploceidae, or Old World seedeaters. These names indicate the probable origin of each family, and also where the bulk of the species still occurs; however, representatives of each family have invaded the other's domain.

In North America the fringillids include the cardinal finches (cardinal, pyrrhuloxia, most grosbeaks, and three buntings—painted, indigo, and lazuli), and the sparrows (towhees, juncos, longspurs, and the large number of species that are called by the name of sparrow). The ploceids are represented by the goldfinches, purple and house finches, pine grosbeak, crossbills, and siskin. Another ploceid finch that is common in North America, although not in the wild state, is the canary, originally a native of the Canary Islands off the African coast.

The finches are thought to have evolved relatively recently, because the seed-producing plants on which they rely were not abundant until the Miocene Epoch. Since that time, the plants have spread, and so have the finches. The worldwide distribution of these birds and the many species, as well as their successful utilization of so many habitats, have led the ornithologists to consider them to be the most successful group of the entire class to which all birds belong.

Among the finches native to North America, the male of the pair helps with the nest building. Generally, he does not assist with the incubation, but he may carry food to the female, and he shares the rearing of the young. The nestlings are fed on insects, although the adults of a few species—the black seedeater, for example—regurgitate partly digested seeds to feed the young.

A famous group of finches of 14 species has been named for Charles Darwin, the English scientist who in 1853 visited the Galapagos Islands, where the birds live. Some of Darwin's finches eat only insects, others feed upon fruit, some bore in wood for grubs, but internal evidence proves that all are of one parent stock. His interpretation of this discovery helped him formulate his theory of evolution.   —G.B.S.

House Finch

Other Common Names—Crimson-fronted finch, red-headed linnet, linnet, burion, redhead

Scientific Name—*Carpodacus mexicanus*

Family—Fringillidae (grosbeaks, finches, sparrows, and buntings)

Order—Passeriformes

Size—Length, 5½ inches

Range—Nests in the lower altitudes from British Columbia, Idaho, northern Wyoming, and western Nebraska, south through California, New Mexico, Arizona, central Texas, and western Kansas into Mexico. Introduced into New York City area about 1940; also introduced into Hawaii. Small groups of house finches now nest on Long Island and in Westchester County, New York; also in southwestern Connecticut. Winters in breeding areas

The house finch is a native western bird. It seems to get along wherever it goes—in the desert, canyons, foothills, river valleys, and along the coast. The big cities and ranches of the West are another environment to which they have adapted themselves. The only really critical need of the house finch appears to be water. In dry desert country the presence of the house finch is one of the surest signs that a spring or cattle tank is not far away. Around streams that do not run dry, groups of house finches often are the most noticed birds.

Purple finches (male, above; female, below)

They fly over the rough boulders of the canyon walls, pausing to rest on the top of some bush where they sing a few snatches of their cheerful song.

The house finch is a bright note in the barren desert, and though they can survive there, they seem to prefer land where man has made his home. They like lush agricultural country, well-watered and green. They like gardens with their bright flowers; vines that cover the walls; and the many odd corners in buildings. In many parts of the West, the house finch is the commonest bird, and its pleasant voice is the first heard each morning just outside the window. Both the red males and the gray females sing, but the song of the female is more modest, not so full-throated and canarylike.

The house finch resembles the purple finch—a bird which really is not purple, but a rich raspberry–red. The purple finch is not as familiar to most people

because it spends much of its time among evergreens. The narrow, dark stripes on the side of the belly of the male house finch are the surest signs of recognition. There are marked variations in the coloration of individual male birds—some are redder than others, in many the red tends toward orange, or even orange-yellow.

The house finch seems to find almost any location suitable for its nest, providing it offers good protection. Buildings are the favorite, though small holes in cliffs are used, as well as abandoned mailboxes, birdhouses, tangles of cactus, and even the old nests of other birds. The female seems to be the sole builder of the compact, straw-built nest. The four or five eggs are a very pale blue-green, almost white. Like the eggs of most finches, they are usually spotted with dark marks, especially around the larger end.

It takes two weeks for the young to hatch, and in a few days the nestlings are feathered out. They are streaked like their mother but with short, stubby tails. Although, occasionally they are fed insects, almost 98 percent of their food is made up of vegetable matter, mainly an enormous amount of weed seeds. —A.B.,Jr.

Purple Finch
Other Common Names—Purple linnet, purple grosbeak, red linnet, gray linnet
Scientific Name—*Carpodacus purpureus*
Family—Fringillidae (grosbeaks, finches, sparrows, and buntings)
Order—Passeriformes
Size—Length, 5½ to 6¼ inches
Range—Breeds from British Columbia, east to Nova Scotia; south to southern California, Arizona, North Dakota; and from northern Ontario to northeastern Ohio, southeastern West Virginia, western Maryland, northeastern Pennsylvania, northern New Jersey, and on Long Island, New York. Winters from southern Canada to Texas, Florida, Gulf Coast, Arizona, and California

The purple finch is not purple but a rich raspberry-red, which is deepest on the breast, crown, and rump. Its bill is heavy and round, approaching in size those of the grosbeaks, while its body size compares with that of the song sparrow and house sparrow — about six inches long. It has a way of raising the feathers of its crown when it is excited.

Since it has such a rich coloring and it is a winter resident in many parts of its range it is curious that the purple finch is not a better known bird. Perhaps it is because the females and young have gray and brown stripes which make them look like sparrows, and the brightly colored male escapes notice because he sings in the trees, where his colors cannot be seen except in bright light. The change in color of the young male finch, from his plain northern garb to the full crimson costume takes two seasons, and the rosy flush does not appear until the end of the second year.

In spite of his unique plumage, it is for his song that the purple finch has won renown, and it is by his song that he is most readily identified. The ideal time to hear him sing is during the nesting season in May and June.

The nest of the purple finch is much like that of the chipping sparrow, but larger. It may be built in an orchard tree, but more often the nest is built on the branch of an evergreen. Fine weed stalks and grasses are used in its construction, and the interior is lined with horsehair. The eggs are green-blue and spotted with dark brown.

Purple finches often travel in small flocks and are somewhat gregarious at all times. They eat many of the seeds of the most destructive weeds, ragweed being a favorite. In their search for weed seeds, they are sometimes rewarded with insects they find on the ground, among them ground beetles and cutworms. The purple finches are particularly destructive to plant lice and cankerworms and also include orchard and woodland caterpillars in their diet. They are also the most confirmed eaters of buds of all native birds.   —A.B., Jr.

FIR
Balsam Fir
Other Common Names — Balm-of-Gilead fir, Canada balsam, blister fir, silver pine

Scientific Name — *Abies balsamea*

Family — Pinaceae (pine family.)

Order — Gymnospermae

Range — Yukon Territory and northern Alberta, east across Canada to Newfoundland and Labrador, south to New England, eastern New York, west to Minnesota and Wisconsin; at high elevations, south to Virginia

Habitat — Coniferous forest belt

Leaves — Stemless needles, an inch or less in length. Fir needles are flat, with blunt tips, usually growing flat, sometimes upcurled and showing the blue-white undersides. Aromatic

Bark — Fairly smooth and gray in young trees, becoming furrowed in older trees. Resin collects in small vesicles on the bark

Flowers — Buds are reddish and very resinous. Bracts narrow at base and oval at tips and slightly serrulate

Fruit — Cones are from two to four inches long, and grow upright on the twigs. They are smoother than the cones of either spruces or pines, and usually disintegrate down to the core by the time heavy snows fall. They are purplish when young

The balsam fir is the only fir that is native to the northeastern portion of the North American continent. It is usually a handsome, symmetrical tree, growing in the form of a long, thin triangle; high winds on mountain tops may limit its growth to that of a stunted shrub. It often grows with the white and black spruces which much resemble it in shape; however, spruces have sharp-pointed needles and pendant cones — the balsam fir has

Balsam fir

blunt needles and erect cones (*See under Spruce*).

Balsam fir resin has a commercial value in medicine, in painting, and other fields. The wood is too light for most uses, but is in demand for pulp. In the East, the balsam fir is one of the best-loved Christmas trees. Grouse, red squirrels, and mice eat its seeds; moose and deer browse on the needles and twigs.

There is one other eastern fir, the Fraser fir, limited in range to the higher elevations of the Appalachians, in Virginia, North Carolina, and Tennessee. Six species of firs grow in the West; the Pacific silver fir ranges from Alaska to California near the coast; the bristlecone fir occurs only in Monterey County, California; the white fir, of great commercial importance and size (to 200 feet in height, 6 in diameter) from Wyoming and Oregon to California and New Mexico; the grand fir, from British Columbia to California; the subalpine fir, from the Yukon to New Mexico; and the Californ-

ia red fir, in Oregon, Nevada, and California.

The Douglas-fir is in a genus all its own, the *Pseudotsuga*. The needles are similar but the cones hang down, their scales stay on all year, and the bracts on each scale give it a fuzzy appearance. It is the third largest tree in the northern hemisphere, yielding only to the 2 sequoias in size, and may attain a height of 200 feet, with a trunk 17 feet around. It is of great economic importance to western lumbermen, and vast areas there have been seeded to this species.   —G.B.S.

FIRE: *Effect on Forests (See under Arborvitae: The Moose Creek Arborvitae)*

FIREFLY

To children, scooting for glass jars, fireflies are lightning bugs, living lanterns, cold fire, stars in the hand. To all lovers of nature, fireflies bring magic to summer's twilight, jewels to the night. Yet few people, young or old, know the true, but no less fascinating facts about these luminous creatures.

Scientifically, fireflies are beetles of the family Lampyridae, a name based appropriately on the Greek word for *bright*. Fireflies live in many parts of the world—although they are almost unknown in England. In the United States there are about 60 of the lampyrid species that glow and about 60 kinds that do not. Each species of firefly has a characteristic light signal, usually in the greenish-yellow range. In Burma and Thailand there are fireflies that gather on certain trees and all flash on and off in unison.

It is now generally accepted that the firefly's light functions to attract the sexes. A common North American firefly, *Photinus pyralis*, uses its light in a way that is typical of many fireflies. The male and female emerge from the grass at dusk; the male flies about two feet above the ground while the female perches a little above the ground such as on a blade of grass. The male emits a

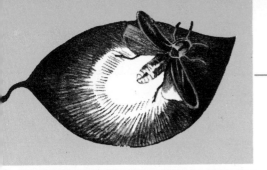

short flash on the upstroke of his flight at regular intervals of about two seconds —more rapidly on a warm evening, slower if it is cool. The female flashes a short response at about six-second intervals. The pair repeat the exchange, usually from 5 to 10 times, until the male reaches the female and they mate.

Many a youngster has lured fireflies into a glass jar with a flashlight. For best results, the flashes should come at carefully timed intervals for they are to simulate the female's flashing. It is the male that is being trapped by this method. The female seldom flies and never flashes until signaled by the male. The male firefly, since it is the active searcher, has better eyesight than the female. Clarity of vision in insects depends on the number of facets in their compound eyes; each eye of a male firefly may have as many as 2,500 facets compared with perhaps only 300 facets in a female's eye.

Fireflies usually flash only in the dusk of evening after sundown, or early in the morning, just before daylight. Under artificial conditions, the flashing period of the firefly may be postponed; once resumed, the flashing will be repeated at 24-hour intervals, no matter what time of day it is.

A common belief in some sections of the United States is that fireflies develop from earthworms. This idea arose, doubtless, from the fact that the firefly passes through a larval stage. The firefly larvae, which already have the light organ, are commonly known as glowworms. The larvae are carnivorous, and eat slugs, snails, earthworms, and larvae of smaller insects. There may be as many as 16,000 firefly larvae in an acre in the tropics. In New Zealand there are caves where thousands of glowworms hang by long luminescent threads. When disturbed, all the larvae turn off their lights at once; the lights gradually come back on after a short period.

Fireflies offer probably the most familiar examples of a natural phenomenon known as *bioluminescence*—light given off by chemical reactions within living organisms. Bioluminescence is found among a wide range of organisms. They include, among others, certain bacteria, fungi, sponges, corals, clams, snails, squids, centipedes, and insects. Although some fishes are self-luminous, the phenomenon does not occur in any amphibians, reptiles, birds, and mammals, nor in any of the higher plants. It is worth noting, too, that no freshwater organism—with the possible exception of some bacteria—is luminous, even though many are close relatives of saltwater organisms that emit light.

The firefly's flash is probably triggered by a nerve impulse delivered to the luminous gland at the end of the abdomen. A sequence of chemical reactions then occurs, but the basic combination involves oxygen from the air and a light-emitting substance called *luciferin*. Another chemical substance, *adenosine triphosphate* (ATP) is also consumed in the reaction. Furthermore, the reaction must be catalyzed by a third substance, an enzyme called *luciferase*. The firefly's light produces no heat and so deserves its name *cold light*.

Although there are many differences in the reactions and substances involved in the various luminescent organisms, the basic process is probably much the same. The most authoritative theory today is that the origin of the light-emitting process was associated with the early evolution of life on earth— probably as a means of removing oxygen from the organism. Eventually organisms developed that could use the oxygen but the light-emitting process remained. In some cases, such as the firefly's mate-attraction, the process evolved into a practical use.   —N.W.E.

Beach grass lines the ocean front at Fire Island National Monument

Wild roses are common stabilizing plants on Fire Island dunes

FIRE ISLAND NATIONAL SEASHORE

Location—Long Island, New York
Size—5,700 acres
Mammals—Deer, foxes, minks, muskrats
Birdlife—Mute swans, geese, ducks, skimmers, gulls, terns, songbirds
Plants—Red cedars, red maples, tupelos, sassafras, a unique forest of holly

Fire Island is a barrier beach, a low ridge of sand facing the Atlantic Ocean on the southern shore of Long Island. Low dunes, back from the shore, rise to 40 feet, but much of the area is barely above sea level. The marshes on the shoreward side form an excellent habitat for ducks and shorebirds.

Accommodations—In nearby towns.
Headquarters—On Fire Island

Fireweed

FIREWEED

Other Common Names—Great willow herb, wickup
Scientific Name—*Epilobium angustifolium*
Family—Onagraceae (evening primrose family)
Range—Eastern North America south to North Carolina, west to Black Hills, South Dakota, Arizona, and California
Habitat—Dry soil in open places
Time of Blooming—June to September

This plant, which has tall spikes of purple-lavender or occasionally white, flowers, has gained its name because it commonly springs up after fires on burned-over forest areas. The change in soil conditions, brought about by a forest fire, will stimulate the growth of fireweed to such degree that where there had been only a few plants a dense growth will appear within a year or so. The great quantity of small seeds produced by each plant, and their dispersal via their hairy "parachutes" carried on the wind, guarantees them wide dispersal and readiness to grow prolifically.

Fireweed is a member of the evening primrose family, which commonly has yellow flowers. It has four large petals and four narrow sepals about the same color as the petals attached at the top of the long style. There are eight stamens and a four parted stigma. The seed pods are long and four-angled. When the seeds are ripe the pod starts to split at the top and the small seeds are launched one by one into the air.

The plant often reaches a height of eight feet. A near relative, which lives in the western states and Alaska, grows to even a larger size and has slightly larger flowers but they are the same color as the eastern species.

FISH

Fishes are water-dwelling vertebrate animals that breathe through gills—comblike tissues filled with blood vessels—that effect the interchange of waste gases for the oxygen in the water. Because they lack internal mechanisms for raising the body temperature above that of their environment, fishes are said to be cold-blooded. All but a few of the 17,000 to 20,000 species in the world (about 4,000 species in North American waters) have fins; one or more dorsal fins along the back, a pair of pectoral fins just in back of the head, a pair of pelvic fins below and often behind the pectorals, an anal fin on the underside near the tail, and a caudal, or tail, fin. Some fishes live only in fresh water; others in salt water; a few live in warm water; others only in cold water.

The sense organs of fishes correspond in general to those of the other higher animals. Their eyes are variable in size and efficiency; some cave dwelling fishes (*see under Cave Life*) and some fishes of the ocean depths are eyeless, but those living near the surface and some that live at great depths have well developed eyes capable of good vision at short distances and with some color perception (*See also Animal: Color Vision in Animals*).

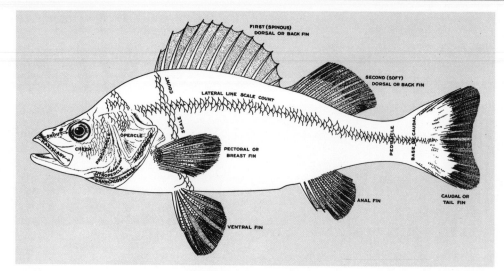

Topography of a fish

Although they do not have external ears, fishes are very sensitive to vibrations. These are detected by sensitive cells along the lateral line, which extends over the top and side of the head and the side of the body to the base of the tail, and by connections between the swim bladder and the inner ear in some species. In the latter, the swim bladder, a sac filled with oxygen and nitrogen and located between the backbone and the intestines, is believed to amplify sound waves. The swim bladder's chief function is to give the fish control over its own buoyancy. The comparatively few species that can breathe air usually manage to use this organ somewhat as a lung. It is lacking in sharks and rays, and in the bottom-dwelling flatfishes, among others (*See under Sharks, Rays, and Chimeras*).

The body plan of fishes is an ancient one. Traces of fishlike creatures appear in rocks of the Ordovician Period, 500 to 425 million years ago, although the fossils are too incomplete to reveal much data. Fishes with a notochord and skull, but without a lower jaw, were not uncommon in the Silurian Period, 425 to 405 million years ago. Their jawed descendants, further evolved and greatly diversified, were the dominant life forms in the Devonian Period, 405 to 345 million years ago, in the great age of fishes (*See under Geological Time*).

Many features common to all the higher animals appear first among the fishes, such as the backbone, two pairs of limbs, bones, and teeth. The ancestors of the amphibians were some of the lobe-finned fishes; reptiles evolved from some of the amphibians, and both birds and mammals derive from reptilian stock.

Because they possess a backbone built around a notochord, fishes are members of the phylum Vertebrata, with the other highly developed animals; within the phylum there are four fishlike classes: Amphioxi, Agnatha, Chondrichthyes, and Osteichthyes. The first class, Amphioxi, includes only the lancelets. The living members of the class Agnatha, the lampreys and the hagfishes, do not have the pectoral and the pelvic fins, and their poorly developed backbones are of a cartilagelike substance, not bone; they are the only parasitic fishlike vertebrates. The class Chondrichthyes, the sharks, rays, and chimeras, also have a cartilaginous skeleton, and have toothlike scales (dermal denticles) instead of the flat, ornamented scales of the true fish.

The class Osteichthyes contains the true, or bony, fishes, gill-breathers with a bony, not cartilaginous skeleton, flattened scales, and with paired fins having bony supports.

Within this class there are three subclasses that are quite different from one another, and in remarkable ways.

The lungfishes, or Dipnoi, of the modern world live in a limited region of Australia, in muddy rivers; in most African rivers south of the Sahara; and in swamps in tropical South America. Their ancestors, in the Devonian and later periods, ranged through the warm seas of the world. All six living species (four are African) have the ability to burrow in mud as the river or swamp dries up, to breathe air through a small hole in the top of the burrow and to maintain their body metabolism by absorbing their own muscle tissue. The air is carried directly to the large swim bladder, where oxygen passes into the fishes' bloodstreams.

The lobe-finned fishes, or Crossopterygii, are also ancient, and their fossils are found in Devonian rocks all over the world. They were thought to have become extinct 70 million years ago in the Upper Cretaceous until living specimens of a single species were discovered off South Africa, the first in 1938. The most remarkable thing about these fishes is that the pectoral and pelvic fins are on stalks of muscle and bones. The first of the amphibians is believed to have evolved from a similar stock.

The third group, that of the ray-finned fishes, or Actinopterygii, contains the bulk of the living fishes. It is also an ancient group, widespread in the Devonian, but probably more in the Cretaceous and later periods. The sturgeons, paddlefishes, gars, the bowfin, and all of the teleosts, or modern bony fishes, are in this group.

Most of the teleostean orders, of which there are 33, arose in the middle to late Mesozoic and quickly crowded out many of the older forms. Today these modern fishes account for more than 95 percent of the total of individuals.

The first great order of modern fishes is that of the clupeiform fishes, primitive forms resembling the bowfin in many ways. The fins have soft rays, lacking in spines, the scales are thin, overlapping, and disklike, and the vertebrae are hourglass-shaped. Most of the ancestral Actinopterygii of the Upper Paleozoic and Lower Mesozoic lacked bony vertebrae and had placodelike scales.

Tarpon, a modern clupeiform, and best known as a game fish, is common in warm Atlantic waters and in the Pacific. Herrings, shad, menhaden, and sardines are generally small, with oily flesh, and feed upon the animals of the plankton; they swim in schools, frequently in astronomical numbers, and are important commercially. The salmons, trouts, and whitefishes are edible species; the annual spawning migration of salmon is a common feature of rivers in the northern part of the continent, where exploitation, dams, and pollution have not exterminated the fishes of the streams.

Smelts are a group of saltwater fishes, although one freshwater species is found in the Great Lakes in large numbers. The pikes, including the pickerel and the muskellunge, are freshwater predators, lean and swift; the record muskellunge weighed 102 pounds (*See under Pike*).

The myctophiform fishes are the lizard fishes, with reptilian heads and slender bodies, and the deepwater lantern fishes and pearleyes, among others. Lantern fishes, with rows of luminescent organs on the sides, are about four inches long, the others are often larger.

Minnows, carps, dace, suckers, characins, and catfishes are grouped together in one order because they all have a series of small bones connecting the ear, which is internal, with the swim bladder.

Only the sea catfishes, which have barbels, or feelers, in typical catfish fashion, and one minnow, are marine. This large order is known as the Cypriniformes.

The fishes in the order Anguilliformes (needle-shaped) have lost one or both of the paired fins and are exceptionally long and thin. They are the eels, which include the edible American eel (*see under Eel*) that spawns in the Atlantic yet lives most of its adult life in freshwater streams, and the morays, conger eels, snake eels, and a few other saltwater families.

Needlefishes, halfbeaks, and flying fishes almost always have soft-rayed fins, the dorsal and pelvic fins are set back near the tail, and there are unique features in the jawbone; together with the killifishes and silversides they form the order Atheriniformes. The needlefishes have both jaws extended, pointed, and studded with sharp teeth; halfbeaks have a short, rounded upper jaw and a long, projecting lower jaw; the flying fishes have two blunt jaws, but have lengthened and widened pectoral fins with which they glide over the water (*See under Flying Fish*).

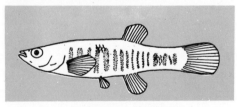

Freshwater killifish

Killifishes or topminnows are common in fresh water, and some species live in both fresh and salt water. A number of species are common aquarium fishes, such as the guppy, the mollies, and the gambusias (*See under Aquarium*).

Codfish and hake, species of considerable commercial importance, and the deepwater grenadiers or ratfishes, make up the order Gadiformes. The fins are mostly soft-rayed, and the pelvic fins are set forward of the pectorals. Hakes are found only in the Atlantic,

but there are three cods in the Pacific, and one, the burbot, in the Great Lakes (*See under Cod*).

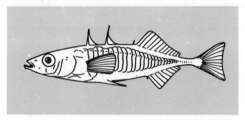

Three-spined stickleback

Sticklebacks, trumpetfishes, pipefishes, and seahorses have bony external plates and unusual breeding habits. Male sticklebacks build the nest and guard the young, while seahorses and pipefish males carry the eggs in a pouch after the females have laid them. Sticklebacks live in fresh or salt water; the others are marine. The ordinal name is Gasterosteiformes.

The order Lampridiformes is composed of a few deepwater species of dissimilar appearance. They have a peculiar jaw structure that establishes their mutual relationship. The opah, or moonfish, is six feet long, weighs more than 500 pounds, and is less than 6 inches wide. The oarfishes may be 30 feet long, 3 inches wide, and crested with red spines. Ribbon fishes are similar, but even narrower.

Squirrelfishes and the beardfish are deep-sea fishes of nocturnal habits, usually with big eyes. The order is Beryciformes.

Troutperch, sandroller, and pirate perch, of the order Percopsiformes, are small freshwater fishes with spines preceding the dorsal, anal, and pelvic fins.

The order Perciformes, that of the perchlike fish, is the largest order in the class. Variety of shapes, sizes, and habits is great, but all members have the pelvic fins set far forward, and each of these fins has a spine and five soft rays; there are usually two dorsal fins — the first spiny, the second soft.

One group of families of this order

includes such edible fishes as the salt-water porgies and scup, snappers, grunts, butterfish, groupers and sea basses, such marine game fishes as snook, cobia, bluefish, jacks, pompano, and dolphins, and the colorful wrasses, parrotfish, and angelfish. Close relatives, living in fresh water, are the perches, large and smallmouth bass, sunfishes, and darters.

Another group of families within the order of perchlike fishes would be that of the mackerels and tunas. Important both as food fishes and game fishes, these are streamlined predators. The rays of the tail fins overlap the end of the backbone, an arrangement that permits members of this group to transmit more power to the tail and therefore to attain very high speeds. A very large bluefin tuna will weigh about 1,800 pounds and will measure 14 feet long.

Some of the other fishes in the huge perchlike family include barracudas and mullet, the economically valuable butterfish the small but omnipresent gobies and blennies, and the wierd mud-springer that scampers about on beaches out of water in search of food.

The bizarre and sometimes poisonous scorpionfishes are sometimes included in the perchlike group, with related forms such as rockfishes, searobins, sculpins, and the flying gurnard, that walks on the bottom with the forward rays of its enlarged pectoral fins, and glides on the membranous surface of the rest.

The order Pleuronectiformes contains the flatfishes, such well-known species as halibut, flounder, sole, plaice, and turbot. The young flatfish adheres to the customary posture, dorsal fin upright, ventral fins downward, one eye on each side of the head, and the mouth below and between them. Before it is more than a few days old, one eye starts to move up and over the top of the head, finally coming to rest on the other side. At the same time the eyeless side turns over to become the underside, without pigment, while the side with two eyes is now the top. In some species the left eye moves, in others the right, and in a very few species either eye may make the journey (*See under Flounder*).

A small order, with only eight species that touch the shores of the United States and Canada, is that of the remoras, the fishes with the suction plates on the top of the head; these they use to attach themselves to sharks, whales, or turtles for free rides. The name of the order is Echeneiformes.

The order that contains the trigger-fishes, trunkfishes, filefishes, porcupine fishes, and puffers, also has the ocean sunfish, an apparently tailless 2,000-pound monster with a skin two inches thick and weak, soft bones. Trigger-fishes have bony scales and two sharp spines forward of the dorsal fin; the first spine can be manually depressed only after the second, and smaller one, the "trigger," has been pushed to release the locking mechanism. Puffers are named for their defensive habit of inflating themselves with water or air when attacked. Porcupine fishes are puffers with the addition of spines. These fishes are in the order Tetraodontiformes.

The last two orders contain some of the ugliest fishes in the entire class. In the Batrachoidiformes, the toadfishes are bottom fishes, dark in color, studded with short spines, and with wide, wicked, dagger-jawed mouths. The angler, or goosefish, in the order Lophiiformes, is similar, but flatter; it may reach 70 pounds, and has actually been known to catch, and swallow, full-grown geese. It is an angler, a fish that possesses a lure growing out of the head and above the capacious mouth; small fish, drawn to the lure, are seized by the goosefish. Frogfishes and bait-fishes, in the same order, are mostly lumpish and dark-hued; they too have fishing lures. They are poor swimmers, creeping or actually jumping over the bottom or on floating sargassum weed with the stubby pectoral fins.   —G.B.S.

Common Freshwater Fishes of North America

With few exceptions, the name fish is given to all animals that live in water, breathe by gills, and possess fins. All the freshwater fishes discussed, with the exception of the yellow perch and the pickerels, may be kept with some success in a balanced aquarium (*See Aquarium*).

Catfish, Bullhead, or Horned Pout, Ictalurus nebulosus

The large catfish is abundant in still waters and sluggish streams. It can be recognized by the large blunt head with its 8 prominent barbels. Specimens 18 inches long are found, but the average size is much smaller (*See under Catfish*).

Johnny darter

Johnny Darter, or Tessellated Darter, Etheostoma nigrum

To its habit of moving in swift and sudden lunges, and to the markings that give it a checkered appearance, this fish owes its name. It can be found resting on the gravel of fast moving streams, but it is often difficult to see because of its protective coloring.

Blace-nosed Dace, or Brook Minnow, Rhinichthys atratulus

The dace may be distinguished by the bold black line which runs from the tip of the snout to the base of the tail. It lives in clear cold streams and brooks, where it reaches a length of three inches.

Yellow Perch, Perca flavescens

Generally considered the most typical of our fishes, yellow perch are abundant in our streams and ponds. The average size is less than one foot. The color is dark green on the back; the sides are yellow, with from six to eight dark, broad, vertical bands that extend a little more than half way down (*See under Perch*).

Miller's Thumb, Mottled Sculpin, or Mufflejaws, Cottus bairdi

The miller's thumb eats the roe (eggs) of all other fishes that live with it in the same stream. Fishes usually lay many eggs — generally far more than necessary to sustain their numbers — therefore predation on fish eggs is not usually harmful to the species preyed upon (*See Predator*). Like the darter, the miller's thumb is protectively colored and lives on the bottom. It reaches a length of six-inches.

American Eel, Anguilla rostrata

The eel is abundant in both fresh and salt water. For hundreds of years strange beliefs existed about the life history of this snakelike fish, and very recently, after long years of speculation, science has replaced curious superstitions with facts. We know now that every spring, adult eels migrate from inland lakes and streams to the open ocean and on to the spawning grounds, an area southwest of Bermuda. There, in the autumn, the eggs are laid and the adults die. The young do not resemble their parents, but are thin and transparent, with cigar-shaped outlines. The larvae leave their birthplace and migrate back through the ocean to fresh water. In April, when they reach our shores, the elvers have already taken the form of mature eels (*See under Eel*).

Banded Killifish Fundulus diaphanus

A resident of small streams and ponds, this fish occasionally strays into salt water. It closely resembles a saltwater form, the mummichog, *Fundulus hetero-clitus,* but it is a slimmer and smaller fish. Males have about 20 silvery vertical bands on their sides; females have between 15 and 20 dark vertical stripes that are thinner and shorter than those of the male.

Three-spined, or European Stickleback, Gasterosteus aculeatus

The three-spined stickleback lives in both fresh and salt waters, and along the Atlantic and Pacific coasts. It may be recognized by a small spine together with two more prominent ones on the dorsal surface. It is a most interesting fish because of its habit of building nests of weeds that are cemented together with threads secreted from the kidneys of the male. Eggs are fertilized inside the nest where they are often guarded by the male fish.

Sunfish, Pumpkinseed, or Bream, Lepomis gibbosus

The sunfish is the best known of our native fishes. In the fresh, clear ponds and streams where it abounds, the sunfish fans away the debris and constructs a shallow pit in the sand in which to lay its eggs. This occurs in early June. In the latter part of the month the fry may be seen swimming in schools with the male fish watching over them.

Golden Shiner, or Roach, Notemigonus crysoleucas

Usually found associated with killifishes, catfishes, and sunfishes, in sluggish or still waters, adult golden shiners may be identified by the deep compressed body and decurved lateral line. Maximum length is one foot. Young fishes do not exhibit the characteristics of mature specimens and can only be distinguished from related species by technical characteristics.

Eastern Mudminnow, or Rockfish, Umbra pygmaea

This fish gets the name *mudminnow*

Yellow perch

from its habit of living in the mud of lowland streams, swamps, and ditches. It is often found buried in half-dried mud. Although never exceeding a length of five inches, it is very ferocious and will not hesitate to attack larger fishes. The color is dark, with 10 to 12 pale stripes running lengthwise, and a black bar at the base of the tail.

Chain Pickerel, Green Pike, or Jack, Esox niger

The chain pickerel is often found lurking in the weeds at the edges of lakes. Its greenish body is covered with many thin horizontal lines which form a reticulated, or meshlike, design. Specimens up to two feet in length are found (*See under Pike*).

Redfin Pickerel, Banded Pickerel, or Barred Pickerel Esox americanus

Banded pickerels inhabit the streams and ditches of the eastern seaboard. The color is light to dark green, with about 20 dark, curved, vertical stripes. Specimens over 10 inches are not common.

Recommended Reading

Along the Brook—R.T. Fuller. John Day.
Field Book of Ponds and Streams—Ann Morgan. G.P. Putnam's Sons, New York.
Fishes of the Vicinity of New York City—J.T. Nichols. American Museum of Natural History, New York.
Living Fishes of the World—Earl S. Herald. Doubleday & Company, Inc., New York.
The Marine Fishes of New York and Southern New England—Nichols and Breder. New York Zoological Society.

*Some common freshwater fishes of
North America*

Carp

Great northern pike

Common bullhead

Grass, or mud pickerel

Chain pickerel

Pike perch

Muskellunge

Yellow perch

Common sucker

Smallmouth bass

Brook trout

Brown trout

Lake trout

Rainbow trout

Sockeye, or red salmon

Landlocked, or Atlantic salmon

Eel

White perch

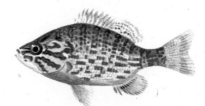

Common sunfish

Striped bass

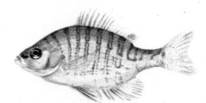

Bluegill sunfish

Largemouth bass

Common Marine Fishes of the North Atlantic Coast

In a world, unseen by most of us, beneath the surface of the salt waters of the ocean; live many kinds of fishes. These animals, whose study is neglected by many people, except for the species they eat, lead intensely interesting lives. For example, at least two hundred and fifty kinds swim in the salt waters within fifty miles of New York City. Some of the most common of the saltwater fishes of the Atlantic Coast are:

Sharks

Comparatively few fishes of the northern Atlantic coastal waters bear their young alive; most of them deposit their eggs in the water, where they are fertilized and hatch. The local sharks, however, are the exception. All of the sharks commonly occurring off New York bear their young alive. The young look like smaller editions of the adult fishes and are able to take care of themselves at once.

Sharks are generally supposed to be fierce and dangerous fishes. This is probably because most of them are very large, very swift, and always hungry. They are great consumers of smaller fishes, crabs, squids, lobsters, and almost anything else they find in the ocean. As a rule they do not attack swimmers, but it would not be prudent to swim among them, for a cornered animal of any kind is apt to attack the nearest person.

One can tell a shark immediately from any other fish by its gill openings. Other fishes have only one gill opening which is under the gill cover. Sharks have five or more, which are to be seen as slits on each side of the body. At the aquarium, one will observe that the skin of a shark is not covered with scales, like that of other fishes, but with minute, hard bumps. The chief internal difference between sharks and other fishes is their skeleton, which instead of being bony, is composed of cartilage or gristle. In examining a shark's jaw one finds another peculiarity—the teeth. In nearly all fishes, when one set of teeth wears down or falls out, others grow out from those sockets to replace them. In the sharks, however, the replacement teeth are visible. They grow in parallel rows to the inside of the row in use, and often one may see six or seven rows of them in various stages of growth. When the front row that is being used falls out, another row moves forward to take its place.

·The well-known and much feared white shark, or man-eater, *Carcharodon carcharis,* a fish usually confined to waters warmer than the northern Atlantic, and the usually more northern basking shark, *Cetorhinus maximus,* both grow to 45 feet in length; common sharks of the northern Atlantic are not as large as this. The smooth dogfish, *Mustelus canis,* the spiny dogfish, *Squalus acanthias,* and the young of the smooth hammerhead shark, *Sphyrna zygaena* (the adults of this shark are not found in northern Atlantic waters), run about two feet long; the sandbar shark, *Carcharhinus milberti,* and the sand shark, *Carcharias faurus,* usually are around four or five feet in length. The hammerhead is easy to recognize because of its head, and the sand shark is a warmer, deeper brown than our other local sharks which are sandy or grayish. Also, in the sand shark, the gill slits are all in front of the pectoral fin. The spiny dogfish is so called because it bears a single spine in front of each dorsal fin. One of its favorite foods is jellyfish. Its flesh tastes strongly of ammonia. The sandbar shark prefers bottom-dwelling fishes, like the flounder, as food. The smooth dogfish and the sandbar shark are harder to recognize on sight, but if the shark one has caught is not one of the others mentioned, it is rather certain to be one of these two. The chief difference between the two is that the smooth dogfish has very blunt teeth, whereas the teeth of the sandbar shark are sharp.

Some common marine game fishes of the Atlantic Coast (following three pages

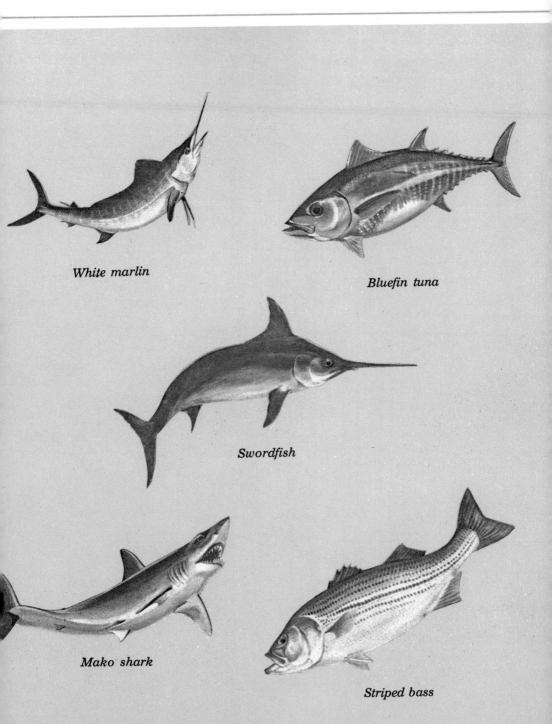

White marlin

Bluefin tuna

Swordfish

Mako shark

Striped bass

Weakfish

Sea bass

Kingfish (whiting)

Porgy (scup)

Blackfish(tautog)

Cunner

Winter flounder

Fluke (summer flounder)

Oceanic bonito

Pollock

Common bonito

Bluefish

Albacore

Cod

Atlantic mackerel

Blowfish (sea squab)

The dorsal fins of the smooth dogfish are the same size; the second dorsal fin (the one nearest the tail) of the sandbar shark is no longer than the anal fin and lies directly over it. All these sharks except the spiny dogfish are in northern Atlantic waters from July to October. The spiny dogfish is found locally in spring and fall, traveling about in great schools deep in the water. Its whereabouts in other seasons is unknown.

Striped Bass, Roccus saxatilis

When autumn comes, all along the Atlantic coastal beaches one sees men in hip boots standing at the water's edge with fishing rods in their hands, casting far out into the surf. They are fishing for one of our finest food and game fishes, the striped bass. This fish is easy to tell from others because seven or eight dark stripes run lengthwise along the greenish-silvery body. Striped bass feed on other fish, crabs, or lobsters. They come into the bays and rivers to spawn. Besides living in northern Atlantic waters, the striped bass lives along the Pacific Coast and occurs in fresh waters (*See under Bass*).

Bluefish, Pomatomus saltatrix

From May to October, the bluefish is in northern Atlantic waters, but it goes farther south to spend the winter. In the bays one finds smaller bluefish, but offshore are the larger ones, swimming around in large schools in pursuit of smaller fish to which they are immensely destructive. The fish's body is blue above, silvery below, with fine, rough scales. It is strong and swift, an excellent game fish, and a great favorite as food (*See under Bluefish*).

Atlantic Mackerel, Scomber scombrus

Everyone who lives in New York City is familiar with this silvery, long-bodied fish as it lies in the fish store windows. The top part of the body is greenish, marked with dark wavy lines, and behind the dorsal and anal fins there is a row each of very small finlets. It is an excellent food fish and the object of larger commercial fisheries on both the Old World and New World shores of the Atlantic Ocean. It swims in vast schools and there is little danger of the supply becoming exhausted, as the female mackerel produces about 500,000 eggs each year (*See under Mackerel*).

Atlantic Cod, Gadus morhua

The Atlantic cod is a cold water fish and one with which the early history of New England is closely united. Long before the Pilgrims landed on our shores, French and English fishing boats had reported back to their countries that this excellent food fish was available in huge quantities off the northern North American coast. Big fishing fleets, both from this country and from Europe, still go out for this fish. The commercial cod fishing boats usually go to deep cold waters, where there is a great deal of fog, making this fishery extremely dangerous. Cod are caught off New York from September to May. The young are reddish, and the adults brown above and white below, covered with small brown spots. There are three separate dorsal fins. A single cod can produce over nine million eggs a season (*See under Cod*). The cod of the Pacific Coast is the Pacific cod, *Gadus macracephalus.*

Flounders

It is impossible to mistake these perfectly flat, roundish fishes for anything else. In the very young of both summer and winter flounders, the eyes are normal, but as the fishes grow they tend to lie on the bottom on one side and the eye from that side gradually moves over the top of the head and comes to rest beside the other eye. In the summer flounder, *Paralichthys dentatus*, also called the fluke, the eyes and color are on the left side; in the winter flounder,

Pseudopleuronectes americanus, they are on the right side. The underside of both fishes is white and eyeless. The upper side of the summer flounder, abundant here from May to November, is light olive-brown, spotted with white; that of the winter flounder, a permanent resident here, is dark brown, spotted with reddish.

Angler, Lophius americanus

One of the most grotesque fishes in the sea is the angler, or goosefish. The front part of its flat-bottomed, banjo-like head is entirely occupied by an enormous mouth filled with sharp teeth. Above the head, bending down over this mouth is a slender rod, which is really a ray of the dorsal fin, bearing on its tip a small, fleshy tab. The tab is said to be used as bait to lure fishes that the angler feeds upon close to its big mouth. Enormous quantities of eggs are deposited in the water by the female angler, and in summer jellylike violet masses of these float at the surface. These egg masses are often 2 feet wide and 30 or 40 feet long, and may weigh over 30 pounds. The fish belongs to a group that includes some very deep sea fishes, in which the bait tab is luminous, shining through the dark, deep waters in which they live. The angler is dark brown, mottled with white. It is in our waters from October to May, and the formidable jaws are often picked up on our beaches. The angler not only feeds upon other fishes but rises to the surface to attack and swallow wild geese, from which it has gotten one of its common names of goosefish.

Recommended Reading

Field Book of Marine Fishes—C.M. Breder, Jr. G.P. Putnam's Sons, New York.
Fishes—D.S. Jordan. Appleton-Century-Crofts, Inc. New York.
Living Fishes of the World—Earl Stannard Herald. Doubleday & Company, Inc., New York.
Marine Fishes of New York and Southern New England—J. T. Nicholas and C. M. Breder, Jr. New York Zoological Society, New York.

FISH-EATING BIRDS
Value of Fish-eating Birds

In a human society ruled by scarcity, as was the case almost everywhere until the 18th century, it was natural that men should have begrudged the seeming competition of wild animals for the foodstuffs they so much needed for themselves and their families. The wolf, the fox, the hawk, the kingfisher, and the merganser all seemed direct competitors with man, and it seemed logical to assume that if the numbers of these predators were reduced there would be more for man.

Today, even though we live in an affluent society, we have unfortunately retained many of the old prejudices against predatory birds and mammals. These attitudes are prejudices because biologists have learned that predators do not reduce the numbers of their prey significantly, and they are therefore seldom competitors of man. (*See Balance of Nature and under Predation*)

Our new understanding of relationships between fish-eating birds and fishes grew rapidly during the early 1940's. At that time, R. W. Eschmeyer and George W. Bennett pointed out that limitations on the number and size of fish that anglers were allowed to take did not necessarily make for better fishing, as had been assumed all along.

The egg-laying capacity of fishes is tremendous, and a pond's production of large ones depends mainly upon their rate of growth. This in turn depends on water temperature and the food supply. If these are favorable, a pond's fish population can grow despite depletion by the anglers, who may fish only a few weeks out of the year. The result is often a large number of medium-size fish that compete with one another for the available food supply. The resulting shortage of food slows their growth and none of the fishes attains the large size so pleasing to the sportsman. The pond is full of stunted fish and total production is slowed down.

Birds such as this young kingfisher help control the fish population in ponds

This undesirable condition is a result of excessive protection.

The egg-laying capacity of fishes is adapted to the heavy predation rate upon the young that is the rule under natural conditions. Not only do the big fishes eat the little ones, but a host of predatory birds and other animals—mergansers, herons, kingfishers, terns, otters, snakes, and many others—thin the fish population. Of those remaining a certain number grow rapidly and achieve the size characteristic of wilderness waters. Only a few of these big fishes,

A pied-billed grebe tends its nest. These birds feed partly on small fishes

which owing to their size are almost immune to attacks by predators, are needed to keep the waters restocked.

The thinning by fish-eating birds of the smaller fishes is thus fundamentally important, and is only a part of the constructive role that these birds play. Unlike the human fisherman who takes his catch home, the merganser, the kingfisher, the heron, and the tern live about the pond or stream that they fish. After digesting their catches, they eject it into the waters as waste, which fertilizes the pond and stimulates the growth of diatoms and tiny animal life on which the smaller fishes feed, thus increasing the productivity of the particular body of water.

Although the relationships of fish-eating animals to fishes, and fishes to their environment, are complicated in cold northern lakes and streams, in general, fish-eating birds play so important a role in the economy of the waters they inhabit that they make for better fishing in the long run.   —R.C.C.

FISHER (*See under Extinct and Threatened Animals of North America*)

An osprey clutches its prey with sharp talons (Audubon's Elephant Folio)

An American flamingo flock at Big Upper Lake, Inagua, Bahamas

FLAMINGO
American Flamingo
Other Common Names--Red flamingo, roseate flamingo
Scientific Name--*Phoenicopterus ruber*
Family—Phoenicopteridae (flamingos)
Order—Ciconiiformes
Size—Length, 48 inches
Range—Breeds in Bahamas, Cuba, Hispaniola, northeastern South America, Yucatan, and the Galapagos Islands; occasionally some wander to southern Florida and other areas along Gulf Coast

Flamingos—which have the longest necks and legs in proportion to body size of all birds—are among the most graceful of all creatures. They are strong, able fliers, capable of long, sustained flights. Flamingos belong to one family, Phoenicopteridae, which most ornithologists assign to the order that includes herons, storks, ibises, and their allies. Some authorities, however, believe that the flamingos are more closely related to the order that includes ducks and geese; it is interesting to note that this relationship is claimed, in part, because similar feather lice are parasitic on both flamingos and certain ducks and geese.

The scientific name of the flamingo family is based on Greek words meaning *red winged*. Actually, only the American flamingo is a truly red bird. The other five species of flamingos are basically white with various shades of red markings. The rosy-winged, or greater, flamingo lives across Europe and Asia and in northern Africa. The Chilean flamingo, smaller than the common European species and less colorful than the American, lives from Peru to the tip of Argentina. The lesser flamingo forms colonies that total more than a million birds on the larger lakes of southeastern Africa. The Andean and James' flamingo are two smaller species that nest on the salt lakes in the mountains of South America. In general, the food and habitat of all flamingos are the same, even though the birds range from below sea level to 15,000 feet up in the Andes Mountains.

The flamingo feeds on nothing larger than very small mollusks. Usually its foods consist of even smaller microorganisms that it sucks up from lake bottoms in an ingenious way. The flamingo places its shovel-like bill upside down in the muddy ooze and scoops in mud, water, and microorganisms. A pumping movement sets up a suction in the bird's mouth. Then, as it closes its bill, the water and mud are squirted out the side of its bill through a fine fringe of hairs along the edges of its beak.

The food, consisting of water beetles, small gastropods, algae, water fleas, shrimps, red worms, diatoms, and other small animals and plants, is retained between the large, meaty tongue by folding a series of 20, fleshy "teeth" on each side of its upper surface over the food items as the water and mud is ejected from its mouth.

Flamingos indulge in elaborate courtship dances with the male being the dominant performer in the ritual. After the birds have paired off, and actual breeding has taken place, nest building begins. The nests consist of mounds of mud that are 9 to 16 inches high. The mud for these is scooped up by the flamingo with its bill from the bottom ooze and is packed into place with the flamingo's bill and feet. A single egg is laid in the shallow depression in the top.

Both male and female birds take turns incubating the egg that hatches in 28 to 30 days. The young bird, at first, looks like the young of a goose and has short legs, a squat body, and a straight bill. In about 10 days the chick begins to take on the appearance of its elders. The bill begins to curve and the legs slowly become longer.   —G.A.B.

Conservation of the Flamingos of the World

A general interest in the life and survival of the flamingos is now at an all-time high. This is so not only in the Bahamas and Netherlands Antilles, but in more distant India, East Africa, and South America. This growing interest is encouraging, for it is a major purpose of the National Audubon Society's research studies on the flamingo and other endangered species (such as the ivory-billed woodpecker, the roseate spoonbill, the California condor, and the whooping crane) to arouse public concern for their future and public support for their preservation. Even after initial studies are completed and detailed research reports published, further reports from observers around the world continue to add to what is known of these birds.

A good example of this was the new knowledge of the flamingo gained in 1956 and 1957. Although field investiga-

The flamingo is protected by the Bahamas National Trust on Greater Inagua, a West Indian island 525 miles southeast of Miami, Florida

tions undertaken by the National Audubon Society were limited to the West Indies, reports come in from people interested in flamingos throughout the world. A sound reason for this is the obvious fact that flamingos face much the same pressures and problems caused by the expanding human population everywhere. As a consequence, Research Report No. 5 of the National Audubon Society (*The Flamingos: Their Life History and Survival*) published in July 1956, comprised a summary of knowledge of all six species of the flamingos — those living in the high Andes; along the coast of Argentina; in Spain and southern France; in East Africa; and in India; as well as the American species of the Gulf Coast, the West Indies, Yucatan and northeastern South America.

As one would expect, the reports on the various colonies and their success were both good and bad. But the important thing was that people in widely separated portions of the globe were aware of the problems that face their flamingos, and an increasing number of them are doing something about it.

One of the greatest advances of recent years was made in South America, where A.W. Johnson of Santiago de Chile, with Francisco Behn and W. R. Millie, discovered the previously unknown breeding place of the little James' flamingo, *Phoenicoparrus jamesi*. Mr. Johnson had previously provided a great deal of information and advice regarding the three flamingo species inhabiting the Andean region, where he had in earlier years made three unsuccessful expeditions in search of the nesting site of the rare *jamesi*. In the summer of 1956 he received a copy of the Audubon Society's flamingo Research Report No. 5. On pages 30 and 31 he read:

"Thus the mystery that surrounds this strange, three-toed, little highland flamingo today is matched by an equally obscure history that goes back more than a century . . . . The most astonishing fact concerning *Phoenicoparrus jamesi*

is that its habits and nidification (nest construction) have never been described. No actual breeding sites, past or present, are known . . . . Although the fact that *jamesi* has not been observed for so many years may be a result of its isolated range, we cannot but wonder if James' flamingo still survives. At the moment this would seem to be one of the outstanding mysteries of the avian world." As Johnson wrote later: "This was indeed too much of a challenge for even an amateur ornithologist to resist, so in spite of our sixty years and the rigours and inclemency of the terrain to be visited, there was nothing for it but to organize a fourth expedition to the remote Andean region of northern Chile where James' flamingo was originally found."

Accordingly, the party left Santiago on January 14, 1957, and traveling by pickup truck, four-wheel drive vehicle, and muleback covered a distance of 3,125 miles in the next five weeks. In the party were Johnson and his son Bryan, Dr. and Mrs. Francisco Behn, and W.R. Millie. Their plan was to visit every possible flamingo habitat in the mountains of northern Chile, from Salar de Atacama as far as Salar de Surire, close to the Peruvian border. But it was a side trip, across the border into a high, uninhabited section of southwestern Bolivia that resulted in the discovery that was the object of their search.

There, on the shores of Laguna Colorada at 14,800 feet, they found both Chilean flamingos, *Phoenicopterus chilensis*, and Andean flamingos, *Phoenicoparrus andinus*, feeding in great abundance. And then Johnson wrote, "we noticed that in a small group of about thirty flamingos, one bird seemed to be somewhat smaller and whiter on the back than the others." It was a James' flamingo, *Phoenicoparrus jamesi*, with the characteristic brick colored legs and the wide yellow area on the bill. In all, there were three flamingo col-

Chilean flamingo (left); American flamingo (center); greater flamingo (right)

onies in the lake, but due to the extreme difficulty of crossing strips of bottomless slime, Johnson and his party succeeded in reaching only one of them. This one contained approximately 1,500 pairs of Chilean and Andean birds, and not more than 20 to 25 pairs of the rare *jamesi*. Valuable and completely new information was obtained on the field identification of the three forms, and on the comparative size and appearance of their nest mounds and eggs. It is an astonishing fact that all three species were nesting together, one the next door neighbor of another, and with no segregation of any sort.

Until this expedition in 1957 it had been erroneously assumed that the Andean flamingo, *P. andinus,* left the high altitudes in winter and moved to the milder coastal regions. Johnson not only corrected this assumption, but explained how it is possible for these birds to survive winter temperatures that in this region may drop as low as -22° F. In the northeast corner of Laguna Colorada the party found a series of hot springs of volcanic origin. These waters had a steady temperature, day and night, of 71.6° F., while elsewhere in the lake the reading was 53.6° F. According to the local Indians, this corner of the lake never freezes, and it is here that the birds remain through the winter. In addition, Johnson wrote, "At Ascotan and Surire salt lakes, we found similar inflows of warm water and such conditions no doubt exist at other points of the essentially volcanic regions that these flamingos inhabit; it is reasonable to presume, therefore, that it is these ultraspecialized ecological conditions that have given rise to and permit their sedentary way of life and account for the fact that neither *P. andinus* nor *P. jamesi,* notwithstanding their strong powers of flight, has ever been reported from points outside the restricted triangle of frigid and forbidding plateau country that constitutes their known geographic range."

Even during the nesting season the weather can be severe. When the Johnson party was ready to leave the one colony they had managed to reach, and make their way back to the firm ground surrounding the lake, "it was well past 3 p.m. and the usual afternoon thunderstorm had begun. Long before we reached the shore the rain had turned into sleet and then to hail, and on our way back to camp it started to snow. Such is the habitat of the South American flamingos!"

It is evidently common practice for local people of Quechua origin to take flamingo eggs for food, and this has probably been going on for centuries. Still, considering the difficulties involved—transporting the eggs on rafts of llama or sheep hides across the mud and slime to the shore, and then getting them packed and by llama or donkeyback across many miles of rugged country to the villages of the interior—this practice can scarcely result in the extinction of these equally rugged flamingos within the foreseeable future.

If the testimony of the Indians themselves is to be credited, the birds replace their eggs after the initial layings are taken, so that they eventually succeed in hatching their young. The fact that the colonies continue to survive in these same sites year after year, and according to Johnson, exhibit "no tangible evidence of any marked diminution in numbers," suggests that the Indians and the flamingos of these remote heights, both of them relatively indigenous, have come to a sort of understanding in matters of survival. The human population is sparse and too poor as a rule to own firearms, and even for them the great difficulty of access must deter all but the most resolute. The natural wariness of the flamingos also operates in their favor, while in the near future, as Johnson pointed out, "there is little or no likelihood that the terrifying whine of the jet planes, which has so seriously disturbed the life cycle of the American flamingo in the islands of the Caribbean, will ever invade the vast and frigid silences of the remote Andean domain of their South American cousins."

Reports indicate that ceilings established for aircraft over flamingo colonies in the Bahamas are generally observed. However, the 1957 nesting season was a failure throughout the West Indies, apparently from natural causes in every case. At Inagua a lack of even the small amount of rainfall normally expected must have had an unfavorable effect on the food supply. At any rate the flamingos there did not nest, the first failure of this kind in some years.

On the coast of Yucatan it was reported that the first nesting in 1957 was destroyed during the egg stage by high tides brought about by a tropical storm. At midday on June 11, all of the eggs floated away. The birds gathered again at a new site but did not lay a second time. At Bonaire, in the Netherlands Antilles, the nesting pond went dry two years in succession, resulting in a lack of food supplies and the loss of many of the young. The local government was much concerned and requested the Netherlands Foundation for Research to set up a special study of the problem.

A more encouraging piece of news came from Andros Island in the Bahamas, where several hundred flamingos were observed from an airplane during the survey conducted in the spring of 1957. If flocks continue to show up on Andros there seems to be a good chance that funds can be found for the purpose of employing additional flamingo wardens, a precaution that will be essential if a successful nesting is to be assured there. A successful resumption of nesting on Andros, where the historic and once famous sites had been deserted for more than a decade, would be a great achievement in the protection of the flamingo, the national bird of the Bahamas.

From farther afield, a letter in 1957 from Luc Hoffmann, of the Biological Station in the Camargue of southern France, reported that after two poor seasons there had been a good one. This referred to the colony of greater flamin-

A flock of preening American flamingos photographed in the West Indies

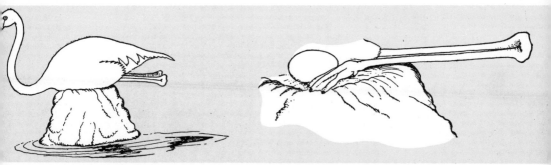

When nesting, the American flamingo rests with its legs doubled up

gos there, the only active nesting group that remained in Europe. The poor results of recent years were due largely to an inadequate policy regarding visitors and photographers. Apparently this has been strengthened, to the benefit of the birds. There are still other troublesome influences, however, and, as Hoffmann writes, "we have to fight against climatic conditions and airplanes."

In East Africa, the outstanding champion of the flamingos has been Leslie Brown, who kept in close touch with the fortunes of both the greater flamingo, *Phoenicopterus antiquorum*, and the more numerous native bird, the lesser flamingo, *Phoeniconaias minor*.

From India Salim Ali of the Bombay Natural History Society reported on the great flamingo colonies in the Rann of Kutch. There had been some concern that a railway embankment built across a section of the Rann had been the chief cause of nesting failures during two or three seasons prior to 1956. The situation was investigated by Ali on behalf of the Indian Section of the International Committee for Bird Preservation. He found that when the monsoon rains resumed at a normal rate the flamingos nested in their usual abundance, in spite of the railway embankment. Excellent nesting resulted in both 1956 and 1957. Normal rainfall is always an outstanding factor in the flamingo's welfare.

Salim Ali's dedication to the flamingos of the Rann was well known among ornithologists. The area was a most dif-

ficult place to reach, but flamingo enthusiasts are a tough lot and difficult to discourage. Because of them and their devotion, the flamingos of the world will have a good chance of survival. —R.P.A.

How the Flamingo Got Its Name

During the Middle Ages, Flanders was the most important principality of the Low Countries. Her artisans and merchants made the region a major financial and industrial center. Many families won great fortunes and lived in high style, with luxurious clothes and furniture.

Portuguese rivals used the word *Flamenco* to designate a native of Flanders. Probably as an international joke that name became attached to a big bird. Its plumage was not especially striking when the long-legged fowl was at rest. But when one took flight, it produced a unique effect. Scarlet coverts of its wings flashed in vivid contrast to black quills of the underwing. It looked almost as gay as a fat Flamenco, resplendent in his fine clothing.

Richard Hakluyt, pioneer English geographer, mastered four languages in order to read books on exploration. Among old manuscripts, he encountered the nickname for the big bird he had never seen. Partly through the influence of his books, *flamingo* became the standard name of the gayly feathered wading bird. —W.B.G.

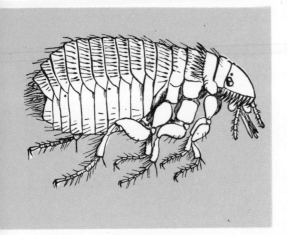

An adult flea

FLEA

Small insects of the order Siphonaptera that feed entirely upon the blood of mammals and birds, fleas become annoying pests and transmitters of such diseases as bubonic plague, endemic typhus, and some forms of tapeworm.

Fleas are ectoparasites that show many adaptations for successful life amid the fur or feathers of their hosts (*See under Parasite*). Their bodies are narrow and deep, and the segments are broadly joined. All six legs are used for walking, but the hind pair, larger than the other two, is used for jumping. They have no wings, and the eyes are reduced or, in some species, entirely missing. One of their mouthparts is a long and pointed beak, through which the fleas suck the blood of their hosts.

The females lay their eggs haphazardly, often among the hairs or on the bodies of the host animals or in the hosts' nests. Cats and dogs spread these eggs about houses, yards, and other places. The eggs eventually roll to the ground, where they hatch into hairy, legless larvae; these feed upon organic debris until they are ready to pupate. The cocoons, hidden in the dust, release the hungry adults after pupation. In some species, the adults never leave the fur or feathers of the hosts; in others, they stay in the hosts' nests, except when feeding. The complete life history of a flea (from egg to adult) in temperate regions may vary from 28 to 42 days.

Fleas tend to be particular in selecting a host; usually, one species of flea will infest individuals of only one species or family of mammals. However, if the customary hosts are not available, substitutes are temporarily accepted.

Among the many fleas that can be named by their choice of hosts are the human flea, the rat flea, the dog flea, and the cat flea. There are six genera of fleas in North America, and more than 200 species. (*See also under Insect*)

—G.B.S.

FLICKER
Red-shafted Flicker
Other Common Names—Walk-up, yawker bird
Scientific Name—*Colaptes cafer*
Family—Picidae (woodpeckers and wrynecks)
Order—Piciformes
Size—Length, 13 inches
Range—Southeastern Alaska, central British Columbia, west-central Alberta, southwestern Saskatchewan and central North Dakota southward along the western edge of the Great Plains to northern Baja California and mainland Mexico to the Isthmus of Tehuantepec

Yellow-shafted Flicker
Other Common Names—High-hole, yarrup, yellowhammer
Scientific Name—*Colaptes auratus*
Family—Picidae (woodpeckers and wrynecks)
Order—Piciformes
Size—Length, 13 to 14 inches
Range—Breeds throughout eastern North America east of the Rocky Mountains and north to the tree limit in Canada and Alaska. Winters from near northern limits of its nesting range (in small numbers) south to southern California, Arizona, Kansas, and from southern New England south to Louisiana

Red-shafted flicker

Yellow-shafted flicker (male, perched; female, in flight)

The patch of white on its rump helps identify the yellow-shafted flicker as it flies away from the observer. Over 125 nicknames are in use for the yellow-shafted flicker in different parts of the United States and Canada—names such as wilcrissen, yellowhammer, harry wicket, high-hole, yocker-bird, and others. Yellowhammer seems to be the most common nickname, not only in the East where the flicker is really a "yellow hammer," but also in parts of the West. The eastern and western flickers are quite different; the eastern flickers show a considerable golden-yellow color in the linings of their wings and tail. The western birds (the red-shafted flicker, *Colaptes cafer*) have red wing-linings instead of yellow, with red "mustaches" on the males. Along the eastern edge of

the Rocky Mountains where the two species share a common habitat, birds are often seen that are hybrids between the two.

The yellow-shafted flicker is a woodpecker, though one that has not taken up woodpecker ways entirely. It often feeds on the ground and, consistent with such a habit, its plumage is a protective brown instead of the usual black and white of most other woodpeckers. Its bill is not stout and chisellike, either. The slight curve indicates it is used more often for poking about anthills than for hacking. Nor is its tongue barbed like a spear. Ants are too small to stab, and the flicker uses other methods. Standing on an anthill it extends its long, sticky three-inch tongue down into the hill, waits until it is swarming with victims, then pulls it in. As many as 5,000 of the little insects have been found in the stomach of one flicker. Although ants make up nearly half the food of the flicker, it feeds on a great many other insects. In the winter it supplements its diet with small berries, such as bayberries and those of poison ivy.

Almost as many interpretations have been suggested for the song of the yellow-shafted flicker as the bird has names. Its common call is a repetitious *wick-wick-wick-wick-wick*. Its "flicker" call is the one given when two birds are together—*flicker-flicker-flicker*. This call is used in courtship—when two or three males try to impress each other and the female with their superiority. A courting flicker hops along a limb, bowing, scraping, swaying, and fluttering by which the bird finally wins itself a mate.

Flickers are wide-ranging birds and will nest wherever there are trees. Although yellow-shafted flickers, like kingfishers, have been known to dig holes in the banks of streams, and even lay their eggs on the ground, they are primarily hole-nesters in the dead limbs of trees. They are skillful and painstaking carpenters. Because of the great amount of time taken in hewing out a suitable home, the flicker is reluctant to give it up. Sometimes the same hole is used year after year, unless a starling or screech owl has established itself before the flicker owner returns in the spring.

The 6 to 10 smooth, white eggs are incubated by both the male and the female. They take turns, but the male takes the night shift. If his mate does not return early in the morning and keeps him waiting a long time for his breakfast he can be heard calling impatiently from the nest cavity.

After about two weeks of brooding, the eggs hatch. The young are blind and helpless at first, but after a few days they are able to cling to the rough sides of the hole. The clamor they raise when they are hungry suggests the buzzing or hissing of bees in a hive, and the noise probably helps keep unwelcome visitors away. The feeding process resembles a sword-swallowing act. The parents regurgitate the half-digested ants into the throats of the young. By the time the young leave the nest, they look much like their parents—more like their father, however, since they all have the mustachial marks at first, just as the male does.

In Canada and along the northern edge of the United States the yellow-shafted flicker is chiefly a migrant. It is one of the early spring birds, moving north with the first bands of robins. In some parts of the Midwest during the spring migration they occur at times in flocks of hundreds. In the fall, great numbers can sometimes be seen at certain places along the Atlantic Coast—such as Cape May, New Jersey, and Cape Charles, Virginia—where they assemble on their way south.   —A.B., Jr.

FLIGHT (*See under Bird*)

FLORIDA BIRDS
Some Birds of Florida

Florida can boast of the greatest gathering of waterbirds in eastern North America. These include not only ducks but herons, gulls, terns, shorebirds, pelicans, and many others.

The National Audubon Society spends many thousands of dollars each year for sanctuaries and wardens in different parts of the United States. A large part of this has been spent in Florida, because rare species, such as spoonbills, ibises, and great white herons especially, need protection there. Conservationists see that this work is always carried on.

The plantlife and soils of the northern part of Florida are much like the rest of the Southeast, but peninsular Florida is quite different. There are many kinds of habitats here—flat woods, hammocks, sandy scrub, swamps, and everglades, salt marshes, beaches, prairies, and keys. Each kind of country has a somewhat different kind of birdlife.

Some of these illustrated are:

1. Florida scrub jay. Locally in scrub oak country, this bird lives in small flocks. It has no crest like that of the Florida blue jay. It is quite tame, sometimes eating peanuts from the hand. The nest, built in a low oak, holds three or four spotted olive-green eggs.

2. Palm warbler. This little bird has a habit of wagging its tail, a good way to identify it. From late September to April it is found in large numbers over most of Florida. It does not sing during its winter stay in Florida; its only sound is a weak *tsip*.

3. Prairie warbler. Male. This species sometimes wags its tail like the palm warbler, but can be told by the black stripes along its sides. It is mostly a migrant, but a race of this bird spends the summer in Florida, especially along the coast, where it nests in mangroves. Its song is a series of thin notes going up the scale.

4. Myrtle warbler. Male. A Canadian that spends the cooler half of the year

Twenty-one typical Florida birds (see text)

in Florida. In dull winter plumage or brighter spring plumage, it can be identified by the bright yellow rump patch. Its call note is a husky *chip*.

5. White-eyed vireo. In dense tangles at the edges of woodlands and swamps, and in scrubby places, the white-eye lives. It can be told by its white wing bars, pale eye and "spectacles." It sings

an emphatic *chick-per-wee-oo-chick*. Another interpretation is *take me to the railroad, quick!* The nest, a shallow hanging basket, is suspended from a crotch in a bush.

6. Gray kingbird. This summering Floridian is seen chiefly at scattered spots along the coast, especially in southern Florida and the Keys. It can be

told from the other kingbird by its pale coloration and plain tail. The nest, built in a tree, is a shallow structure holding four beautifully marked eggs.

7. White-crowned pigeon. In the Florida Keys a large dark pigeon is found during the summer months. When the bird is hidden among the trees its loud cooing or the clapping of its wings as it flies away betrays its presence. It nests in small colonies on isolated keys laying one white egg on a platform of twigs.

8. Red-bellied woodpecker. Male. A beautiful woodpecker with a "zebra back" and a red crown, it is common in woodlands and in towns, excavating its nest cavity in trees or telephone poles, often near houses. Its note is a low *chur.*

9. Nonpareil. Male. This finch, often called the painted bunting, is probably the most brightly colored bird found in North America. The female is a plain greenish color. Nonpareils nest in the northern half of the state, in towns and parks where many trees and shrubs offer the right nesting sites. The male has a bright, ringing song.

10. Blue-winged teal. A small duck with chalky blue patches on the forepart of the wing. The male has a white crescent on the face. It prefers freshwater ponds and marshes, dabbles for its food, does not dive. It is chiefly a wintertime duck.

11. Florida gallinule. Male. A gray ducklike bird with a red bill can safely be called this species. It seems to be half duck and half chicken, swimming well and clucking excitedly when disturbed. The nest is a platform of vegetation in the marsh, with a short runway leading to it. Eight to fourteen freckled eggs are laid.

12. Purple gallinule. Prefers a more bushy type of marsh than the Florida gallinule where wampee, bonnets, and other flowering waterplants grow. It can be told from the other bird by its bright yellow legs, deep purple under-

parts and blue shield on the forehead. The nest is similar to that of the Florida gallinule.

13. Little blue heron. A small, slim heron with a dark slate-blue body and slender legs. Immature birds, which are white, are mistaken for snowy egrets, but do not have yellow feet. Little blue heron's have a preference for fresh water. They nest in colonies with other herons.

14. Swallow-tailed kite. This, the most beautiful of all birds of prey, is now rare outside Florida, where it can still be seen in swampy woodlands, especially in the Everglades and along the southwest coast. It catches insects, snakes, and lizards. The nest is built of moss and twigs, very high, often 100 feet or more from the ground.

15. Louisiana heron. A slender, dark heron with a clear-cut white belly. It has an extremely slender neck which it folds in when flying. It breeds in colonies with other herons, sometimes by the hundreds or thousands. The four or five pale blue eggs are laid on a flimsy platform of sticks. It inhabits both fresh and salt water.

16. Man-o'-war bird. Voyagers in warmer seas often see long-winged black birds, with forked barn-swallowlike tails, soaring with the greatest ease in the wind. These are the man-o'-wars, or frigate birds. They occur off the coast of Florida, especially the southern part of the Keys, using a heron or pelican colony to roost in, but they have never been known to nest in the United States.

17. Black skimmer. A slim-winged bird of the salt water, with a strange, red scissorlike bill, the lower part of which is longer than the upper. Skimmers nest in colonies, often with terns on isolated sandbars or islands, laying three or four heavily blotched eggs in a depression in the sand.

18. Boat-tailed grackle. The big boat-tail, or jackdaw, is found abundantly along the salt water, and on freshwater marshes, too. Females are brown, and are much smaller than the males. Boat-tails are noisy birds with a great repertoire of harsh whistles, clucks, and other sounds. The deep bulky nests, made of grass, are often built in groups in bushes or dense trees.

19. Wood ibis. This stately bird, the only true American stork, can be told from the white ibis by its much larger size, and greater amount of black in the wings. The wood ibis nests in colonies in the more remote parts of Florida. The young in the nest are droll, dignified fellows with large pink bills.

20. Brown pelican. Pelicans are ancient, dignified-looking birds that fly low in ordinary lines over the water. They dive headfirst for fishes, chiefly kinds that have little or no commercial value. They nest in colonies on islands, on the ground, or among mangrove trees.

21. Great white heron. The largest and rarest of North American herons, confined to the southern tip of Florida and the Keys, where a few hundred individuals are safeguarded carefully by National Audubon Society and United States Fish and Wildlife Service wardens. A few years ago they were in danger of complete extinction, but are now coming back. They are longer than the American egret, with yellowish legs. (*See also under Limpkin; Okeechobee; and Corkscrew Swamp*)

Recommended Reading

Florida Bird Life — Alexander Sprunt, Jr. Coward McCann, New York.
[Editor's Note: Past issues of the following periodical publications have many notes and articles about Florida birds.]
Audubon Field Notes. National Audubon Society, New York.
The Auk. American Ornithologists' Union, Inc.
Florida Naturalist. Florida Audubon Society, Maitland, Florida.

FLOUNDER

Many different kinds of flounders are known. All are saltwater fishes, characterized by their extremely flat shapes and by the presence of both eyes on one side of the head. Flounders having their eyes on the left side of their heads are classified in the family Bothidae. Flounders with their eyes on the right are in the family Pleuronectidae. The best known North American flounder is the winter flounder.

Winter Flounder
Other Common Names — Blackback, lemon sole, mud dab
Scientific Name — *Pseudopleuronectes americanus*
Family — Pleuronectidae (righteye flounders)
Order — Pleuronectiformes
Size — Length, up to 18 inches.
Range — Lives in waters along the Atlantic Coast of North America as far north as northern Labrador and as far south as North Carolina and Georgia

The winter flounder's body is oval in outline and typically flat. It is about two and a quarter times as long (to the tail fin) as it is wide. The fish's mouth is small and has thick fleshy lips. A portion of each jaw has a series of close-set teeth. The dorsal fin has 60 to 76 rays. It begins in front of the eye and runs almost to the tail. The anal fin has 45 to 58 rays and is preceded by a short, sharp spine. It runs from slightly in back of the head, almost to the tail fin.

The upper side of winter flounder varies in color depending upon the color of the bottom on which they lay. Usually they vary from muddy shades to reddish-brown, slate, olive, or black. They may be plain, mottled, or spotted darkly. The lower side is white with tinges of blue and, sometimes, yellow. Some of the fins may be tinged with pink, red, or yellow.

Like most flounders, this fish spends nearly all its time at bottom and feeds on small animals and other fishes. It is an important and tasty food fish.

A few of the many other North American flounders include the summer flounder, *Paralichthys dentatus*, and the fourspot flounder, *Paralichthys oblongus*, both in the family Bothidae (lefteye

Flounder

flounder family), and the yellow tail flounder, *Limanda ferruginea*, of the family *Pleuronectidae* (righteye flounder family). (*See also under Fish: Some Common Marine Fishes of the North Atlantic Coast.*) —M.R.

FLUKE (*See Flounders under Fish: Some Common Marine Fishes of the North Atlantic Coast*)

FLY
Housefly
Other Common Names — Disease fly, typhoid fly
Scientific Name — *Musca domestica*
Family — Muscidae (tsetse flies, stable flies, hornflies, houseflies, and allies)
Order — Diptera
Size — Length, one half to three quarter inches
Range — Worldwide

The true flies belong to the order Diptera. Classified within this order are many families (50 are in the United States alone) that flourish in all parts of the world from steamy tropics to the frozen polar areas. The families, in turn, are made up of innumerable species; something like eighty-five thousand have been described (*See Mosquito*).

Some flies are considered helpful because their larvae are scavengers; they eat almost everything of animal or vegetable origin and help keep the air pure by devouring carcasses. Some flies help control pests as their larvae feed on

A detailed drawing of the common housefly shows its tongue that is designed for lapping, and its two-clawed feet under which are sticky pads used for clinging to any surface

such mites as chiggers; some are of service to flowers in aiding cross-pollination; and some adult flies have proved of great value in studies by scientists concerning heredity. Some flies are useful because they furnish food for other animal life, being particularly important for freshwater fishes. But the bad flies cause such trouble that they give the whole group a reputation that is hard to forgive or forget. Actually, some of them are the most dangerous of all animals for on their tiny feet and legs or in the digestive tract they may carry germs of various dread diseases.

Added to the endless variety of true flies we find a number of insects bearing the name that are not flies at all.

Dragonflies, mayflies, and fireflies are a few of them. When we look for the characteristic that sets Diptera apart from other members of the animal kingdom, we find that every true fly has only one pair of wings; all other insects have either no wings at all or two pairs. With the Diptera, in the position where a second pair would belong, there are two little knobs mounted on slender stalks. They are known as halterers, or balances.

Although annoying, the common housefly, *Musca domestica*, is interesting to watch. It can zoom through the air at almost five miles an hour; it can land in almost any position including upside down; it walks upside down across the ceiling as easily as it crosses the floor right side up; it cleans and brushes itself with admirable energy. But the features that make possible those acrobatic accomplishments also make flies the dangerous pests they are. Two tiny pads below the claws are covered with hairs from which oozes a sticky fluid. The sticky hairs make it possible for a fly to cling to almost anything, and it is to them that microbes cling. Diseases as serious as typhoid or dysentery may also be carried in a fly's digestive tract.

With all the potential dangers connected with houseflies, their fantastic ability to reproduce is quite alarming—or it would be if sanitary measures did not keep them under control. Observations have revealed that a female lays her eggs in lots of about 125 each, with the average production of a single fly about 500. Laid as a rule in fermented or moist decaying flesh or matter, the eggs may hatch in less than twelve hours. The larval stage (maggot) that follows lasts only four or five days, and the pupal stage about the same length of time. Then, before long, the new generation of females are ready to start laying. The World Health Organization of the United Nations recently gave out the statistics that, in theory, one female housefly that produced 120 eggs in the spring, by fall could have some 5,500,000,000,000 descendants.

Houseflies are found in practically every country in the world. In the northern regions of the United States the adults mostly die away in the fall, leaving pupae or larvae to survive the cold weather. In the South they remain active and may breed the year round.

The true housefly is blackish-bodied, with stripes of denser black running along the back and the sides shaded in yellow. The large eyes are red-brown. From the time it emerges as an adult, its length is half an inch. All flies when they leave their pupal stage are the size they will always be; small flies do not grow into large ones. Houseflies do not bite; the mouth of *Musca domestica* is designed only for lapping. However, there is a stable fly, *Stomoxys calcitrans*, often mistaken for the housefly, which does bite. This insect frequents barns more than the homes of humans, but at times—especially at summer's approach—they are likely to invade houses.

Biting Flies

The most annoying biters of all make up the family Simuliidae; they are generally called black flies. So determined are they to get blood when they want it, discouragement is almost impossible. They will pursue an intended victim with startling persistence, and once they have gained a footing on the skin, they fearlessly go after their meal. Skillfully they avoid being swatted, and if they must retreat before being satisfied, they return quickly to begin all over again. In areas where black flies are abundant, farm animals suffer severely and may even be tormented to death.

Members of another family, Tabanidae, are appropriately named for the unlucky creatures on which they prey most consistently: they are the horseflies and deerflies. These are common in almost all parts of the world and are distinguished by a large head which looks to be "all eyes." Some species of the Tabanidae family do not bother to attack humans, but some are a serious pest to people. The females buzz around with great persistence, waiting for just the right time to attack—and their bite is sharp and fiery. They may sometimes be seen following large moving objects such as cars and trains, apparently under the impression they are on the track of a juicy victim. When blood is hard to find, they will turn to nectar or pierce plant stems to reach the juices. This vegetable diet is all the male flies require. Though the biting females are a great nuisance and, indeed, may be dangerous in transmitting disease, the horseflies and their allies are not without their useful contribution since the larvae in mud and rotting wood feed upon other troublesome insects. Tabanidae flies are active only in the daytime and sometimes great numbers of them may be seen swarming at sunrise.

Hover fly

Flower, or Hover, Flies

A fly that not only prefers daylight to dark but insists on bright sunshine for its activities is popularly known as the flower, or hover fly. Both names are excellent descriptions; the little insect can hover endlessly over a bloom before it enters it to feed on the pollen and nectar. Syrphus flies are in the family Syrphidae. There are a number of different species of Syrphid flies and, as a whole, they are probably the most colorful and attractive of all the flies. Many of them are marked with orange or cream-white and, in a quick glance, they may look like bees or wasps rather than flies. In fact, this resemblance is believed to be responsible for a myth relating that the carcasses of certain animals generate swarms of honeybees. The insect involved doubtless is one species of Syrphid that breeds in carcasses.

Syrphid flies perform a real service in their visitation of flowers, acting as tireless cross-pollinators. Another habit for which they are appreciated is concerned with their larvae which devour enormous quantities of aphids and mealybugs. A group of them has been seen cleaning swarms of plant lice off the leaves of a currant bush in a fantastically short time. On the opposite side of the ledger we find at least two species that are a menace rather than an aid to gardeners. The narcissus bulb flies, in larval form, feed on the bulbs of these lovely flowers. The larvae of another species, commonly known as the lesser bulb fly, attacks the bulbs of ornamental flowers and of root crops such as onions.

Robber Flies and Fruit Flies

Another fly sometimes mistaken for a bee or a wasp is the robber fly; the error is mostly made when the insect is in flight, for robber flies have a way of buzzing in beelike fashion while in the air. Also, some of them are very hairy like the bumblebee. Robber flies are quite endless in their variety (there are close to three thousand species in the family, Asilidae) and among them are some of the largest flies, many having a length of more than an inch. It is characteristic for them to have a noticeably large head with a strong, lancelike beak, which serves for stabbing and sucking. A narrow abdomen, tapering to the rear, and long legs are also characteristic. A robber fly uses its legs very much in the manner of dragonflies: Swooping at its victim in the air, the "robber" grasps it firmly between the fore feet and carries it off to a swift death. With its sharp beak it stabs the victim, releases a saliva that acts as an anesthetic, and then enjoys its meal. Dragonflies, bees, wasps, and grasshoppers are only some of the items on a robber fly's menu; it even preys on members of its own family. The suggestion has been made that "assassin fly" would be a more fitting name for such a killer, but "robber" is its popular name.

A very tiny fly popularly called fruit

Robber fly

fly is one particularly deserving of notice and admiration. Surely it is a creature that should be considered for trips into outer space. Some years ago an experiment was performed, placing a number of fruit flies in a jar and then, by means of a vacuum pump, decreasing the jar's atmospheric pressure. At the equivalent of eight miles above sea level, the little "space passengers" were walking about quite normally; at seventeen miles above, while they were not moving, none had died. When pressure was brought back to normal, they soon were as good as new.

Other experiments in which fruit flies serve are those concerned with heredity. Their suitability is due to the rapid life cycle they pass through; in ten days they can develop from egg to adult. Many scientists have used them in laboratory work, an especially noted instance being the studies of Professor Thomas Morgan. He succeeded in developing a fruit fly with white eyes instead of the usual red and other color variations, demonstrating with countless generations the physical basis of heredity. Professor Morgan was awarded a Nobel Prize in Physiology and Medicine for his work with these insects.

More than one family of fly is referred to as fruit fly. The one whose members serve science so admirably is Drosophilidae. They are known also as vinegar flies. One will often find them in warm weather swarming about fruits and vegetables, for the adults may lay their eggs wherever they find decaying vegetation. They are attracted also to flowing sap and to fungi. Although we are usually disturbed by the sight of them, these fruit flies are actually considered useful because of their scavenging habits.

Still smaller than the smallest fruitflies are the biting midges a family of flies most appropriately known as *no-see-ums*. So tiny are they, they are felt rather than seen, and their stinging bites are likely to come without warning. The family Heleidae, is widespread and particularly thrives in damp and watery places. In some areas its members are called punkies, in others, sand flies. There seems almost no escape from their unwelcome attentions for they can easily creep through ordinary mosquito netting. The artist, George F. Mason, on his return from Alaska where he had been painting backgrounds for the American Museum of Natural History, gave a dramatic description of these flies which haunted him during the rainy season. Though he smeared "fly dope" over his arms, hands and face, the no-see-ums, undiscouraged, crept into his nose, ears, and eyes. The finished canvases he brought back to the Museum were covered with tiny bumps—the corpses of countless no-see-ums that had been too adventurous for their own good and ended up under his paintbrush.

Crane Flies

Strangely, the fly that is most innocent of trouble-making is one that particularly inspires fear in many people—the larger species of crane fly. The family, Tipulidae, is distinguished by long, slender wings, legs, and bodies—especially are the legs elongated. Because of them these flies are sometimes called "daddy longlegs," and their similarity to the spiderlike daddy longlegs frightens many timid souls. Then there are people who mistake crane flies for unusually large mosquitoes and imagine they will inflict unusually large bites. Fortunately

Crane fly

these flies do not bite at all; on the contrary, they make a contribution to life because the larvae of many species furnish food for fishes.

Many collectors do not regard flies with the same enthusiasm they have for other types of insect life, since most Diptera lack color and are unimpressive in size. Nevertheless there is much interesting variety to observe about members of the group and, considering their impact on our civilization, studying them may prove a really important hobby.　　　　　—D.E.S.

Recommended Reading

Familiar Insects of America—Will Barker. Harper and Brothers, New York.
Handbook of Nature Study—Anna Botsford Comstock. Comstock Publishing Company.
The Insect Guide—Ralph B. Swain. Doubleday & Company, New York.
Insects of the Pacific World—C. H. Curran. The Macmillan Company, New York.
1001 Questions Answered About Insects—Alexander B. and Elsie B. Klots. Dodd, Mead & Company, New York.
Wonders of Instinct: The Bluebottle—Jean-Henri Fabre. The Century Company, New York.

FLYCATCHER

The flycatcher family is well named because the birds that belong to it eat flying insects. From a convenient perch the bird waits patiently until an insect flutters past. A sudden dash, a snap of the bill, and the bird returns to the perch to eat its prey. Then it assumes the typically erect flycatcher posture until the next flying insect appears.

There are 29 species of flycatchers in western North America and 13 east of the 100 degree meridian. Since 10 species are common to both East and West, there are a total of 32 for the continent north of Mexico.

Some of the flycatchers that are common in Central America may be seen in southern Arizona and Texas. The large kiskadee flycatcher, the sulphur-bellied flycatcher, the tiny beardless flycatcher, the dusky Coues' flycatcher, the thick-billed kingbird, and the tropical kingbird appear in the Southwest.

One group of species that resembles one another rather closely is that of the five kingbirds of the genus *Tyrannus*. They are noted for their audacity in driving off crows, hawks, and even eagles. They perch and nest in exposed locations, and the rattling alarm call is often heard in their territory.

The eastern kingbird is rare west of the plains, the gray kingbird occurs only along the southeast coast of the United States, the tropical kingbird is seen along the Mexican border, and both the western and Cassin's kingbird are common through most of the West.

Another genus, *Myiarchus*, similar to the kingbirds but more likely to be seen in woodlands, is composed of such species as the great crested flycatcher, Wied's crested, olivaceous, and ash-throated flycatchers. The first is an eastern species, the last three are western.

A group of 16 smaller flycatchers includes species of the genus *Empidonax* that are very difficult to identify in the field. Such field marks as faint eye-rings and wing bars, the presence or absence of a light yellow tone to the underparts, and the precise quality of the voice are all of importance in identifying these drably colored birds of thicket and woodland. Some of these are the Acadian flycatcher, alder flycatcher, and least flycatcher.

The most brilliantly colored is the vermilion flycatcher, *Pyrocephalus rubinus*; the male is dull black on the back, but has a flaming red crown and underparts. The most unusual flycatcher in North America is the scissor-tailed, *Muscivora forficata*, with tail plumes about three times as long as the body. —G.B.S.

Great Crested Flycatcher
Other Common Names — Crested flycatcher, snake-skin bird
Scientific Name — *Myiarchus crinitus*
Family — Tyrannidae (tyrant flycatchers)
Order — Passeriformes
Size — Length, eight to nine inches
Range — Breeds from Florida and the Gulf Coast north to southern Canada, (Saskatchewan to Quebec), and from the Atlantic Coast west to the Great Plains. Winters from southern Florida and Texas, south to Panama and Colombia

In the East the great crested flycatcher is the only one of the family

Great-crested flycatcher

Least flycatcher

with a rusty tail. The flash of rufous as it darts out from its tree perch after a flying insect is a telling field mark.

The great crested flycatcher is a noisy bird. From the edge of the woods comes its loud, whistled *wheep* with a rising inflection. Its other call is a throaty, rolling *prrrrreeet*. It also has a song that is heard in the dim half-light of dawn— a soft *queedle . . . queedle*, repeated deliberately for a full half hour before sunrise.

The great crested flycatcher is a woodland bird, not a bird of open country like its cousin, the kingbird. It has adapted itself to civilization and often nests in the hollows of trees in gardens of towns. To survive these days, when growing networks of roads, farms, and towns are spreading over the world, a bird's adaptability is often a critical factor in its continued survival. The crested flycatcher does not limit its nesting to old woodpecker holes and hollow trees but will nest in a birdhouse. Usually it prefers a natural cavity—a rather large one in a knothole or a rotten stub. There it builds a foundation of mosses and lines it with string, grasses, hair, and feathers. Often a strip of shed snakeskin is added to the nest.

Usually five or six eggs are laid. They are oddly marked, with dark blotches and scratches on a cream-colored background. The eggs require about two weeks of incubation before they hatch and another two weeks for the young to leave the nest. From then on they gradually learn the techniques of hunting until they can snap up a passing fly with great skill.

More than nine-tenths of all the food these flycatchers eat consists of insects— beetles, bugs, wasps, flies, grasshoppers, caterpillars, butterflies, moths, dragonflies. In fact, there seem to be very few insects they do not eat. They sometimes sample wild fruits—blackberries, elderberries, chokeberries, or whatever else is available at the time.

The great crested flycatcher migrates southward toward warmer and more insect-saturated latitudes as soon as there is a hint of cooler days. Most of these birds leave the North in September, and it is rare to see one in October. Although a few might linger in Florida, most great crested flycatchers summer in the tropics from Mexico through Central America to the northern edge of the great South American continent.

—A.B.Jr.

Least Flycatcher
Other Common Names—Chebec
Scientific Name—*Empidonax minimus*
Family—Tyrannidae (tyrant flycatchers)
Order—Passeriformes
Size—Length, 5½ inches
Range—Eastern North America west to the Rockies. Breeds from middle United States north to southern Canada. Winters south of United States to Panama and Peru

Bird students often experience difficulty in distinguishing between the least flycatcher and the certain other small flycatchers of its genus. The Acadian and alder flycatchers are those most usually confused with the least flycatcher. However, the least flycatcher is a bird of lawns and orchards and fairly open spaces, whereas the Acadian flycatcher is a frequenter of thick woodlands, and the alder flycatcher's favorite haunts are low, wet areas along streams where alder bushes grow. The least flycatcher lacks the distinct olive tinge of the two other species, and also possesses a characteristic note that reveals its identity. *Chebec* it repeats, again and again, with clear enunciation between its sallies into the air after insects.

The least flycatcher is one of our most useful birds, since it is more closely associated with agriculture than some of the more woodland inhabiting species. It destroys large numbers of wee-

Its pectoral fins extended, a flying fish soars above the water

vils, squash beetles, cucumber beetles, curculios, ants, moths, and caterpillars.

The nest is of plant down and plant fibers, rootlets, and hairs; it is generally built in a crotch, from 5 to 15 feet up. From three to five white eggs are laid.

FLYING FISH

Small fishes of the warm oceans that glide for short distances over the waves are called flying fish. They do not actually fly, as they lack the musculature to use their large pectoral fins for propulsion. Their brief ventures into the air, thought to be a method of escaping predators in the waters below, are accomplished by rapidly swimming below the surface to gain the velocity that carries them for 50 feet to perhaps a quarter of a mile when gliding with the wind. Frequently the tip of the tail remains in the water for at least part of the flight and vibrates rapidly to increase the fish's speed. In most species the ventral as well as pectoral fins are enlarged into planing surfaces.

The true flying fishes belong to the family Exocoetidae, whose members have slender bodies, long tails, and very short jaws. They are predatory, feeding on smaller fishes; in turn, they are eaten by dolphin and mackerel, sometimes by man.

The flying gurnard, with its large pectoral fins, can also glide through the air for short distances, although it does so with less frequency. Two freshwater fishes, one from Africa, the other from South America, can also leave the water for brief glides.   —G.B.S.

FLYING SQUIRREL (*See under Squirrel: Southern Flying Squirrel*)

FOOD CHAIN

One of the best ways of understanding how a wildlife community maintains a balance of nature is by learning what the animals in the community eat, because each animal is linked to every other animal in a *food chain*. Food chains follow a basic pattern with a great many green plants (food-producers) at one end of the chain, a variety of herbivores (plant-eaters) in the middle, and a few large carnivores (flesh-eaters) at the other end.

The most numerous plant-eaters are sometimes called *key-industry* animals because they support, in a direct or indirect way, all the predators, or carnivores, in the community. From the food-producing plants to the large carnivores there may be many steps in a food chain. Ultimately all is reduced to basic raw materials by the final action of bacteria and fungi.

Shown below are a variety of plants and animals that might be included in a typical forest community. The food chain interrelationships are indicated by the numbers under each animal. The numbers refer to any dietary item, whether egg, young, or adult. For example, the earthworm (14) eats grass (3), leaves (6), herbs (7), and decaying matter. In turn, the earthworm is eaten by moles (19), turtles (21), ground—feeding birds (22), shrews (27), snakes (28), frogs (29), and raccoons (33).

Owls
31 (12, 16-20, 22-24, 27, 30, 34, 38)

Bears
32 (2, 4, 9, 11-13, 16, 20, 21, 27, 29, 30)

Raccoons
33 (2, 4, 9, 14, 16, 19-21, 27, 29, 30)

Skunks
34 (7, 9, 16, 19, 20, 2 22, 25, 26, 28-30)

Spiders
25 (15, 16, 26, 30)

Centipedes
26 (16, 30)

Shrews
27 (2, 4, 7, 9, 14-16, 19, 20, 25-3

Twig-feeding Birds
17 (4, 16, 25, 30)

Squirrels
18 (1, 2, 4-10, 17, 22-24)

Moles
19 (4, 7, 14-16, 25, 26, 30)

Mice
20 (2, 4, 7, 9, 15, 16, 25, 26, 30, Carr

Porcupines
11 (1, 2, 6, 7, 9, 10)

Deer (2-10)
13

Earthworms
14 (3, 6, 7, decaying mat

1 Bark

Rabbits
12 (1, 3, 7, 9, 10)

2 Nuts

3 Grass

4 Seeds

There are many more plants and animals in a forest community than in the food chain of any single species in the community. Thus, the earthworm's food chain consists of only three plant items and decaying matter that form its diet and seven predators that feed upon it. But the earthworm's predators belong to other food chains; that is, they eat many other things and are, themselves, items in the diet of other animals. The interrelated food chains in a community are known collectively as a *food web*.

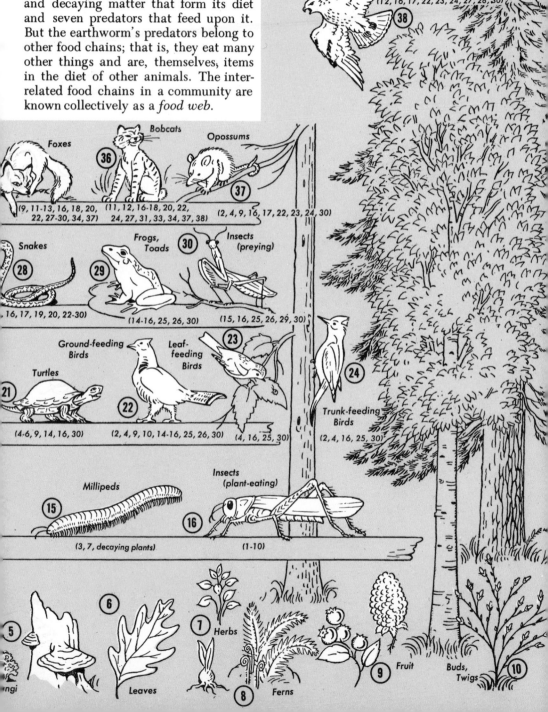

Hawks
(12, 16, 17, 22, 23, 24, 27, 28, 30)
38

Foxes
Bobcats
36
Opossums
37
(9, 11-13, 16, 18, 20, 22, 27-30, 34, 37)
(11, 12, 16-18, 20, 22, 24, 27, 31, 33, 34, 37, 38)
(2, 4, 9, 16, 17, 22, 23, 24, 30)

Snakes
28
Frogs, Toads
30
Insects (preying)
29
16, 17, 19, 20, 22-30)
(14-16, 25, 26, 30)
(15, 16, 25, 26, 29, 30)

Ground-feeding Birds
Leaf-feeding Birds
23
Turtles
21
22
24
Trunk-feeding Birds
(4-6, 9, 14, 16, 30)
(2, 4, 9, 10, 14-16, 25, 26, 30)
(4, 16, 25, 30)
(2, 4, 16, 25, 30)

Millipeds
15
Insects (plant-eating)
16
(3, 7, decaying plants)
(1-10)

5
6
7 Herbs
8 Ferns
9 Fruit
10 Buds, Twigs
ngi
Leaves

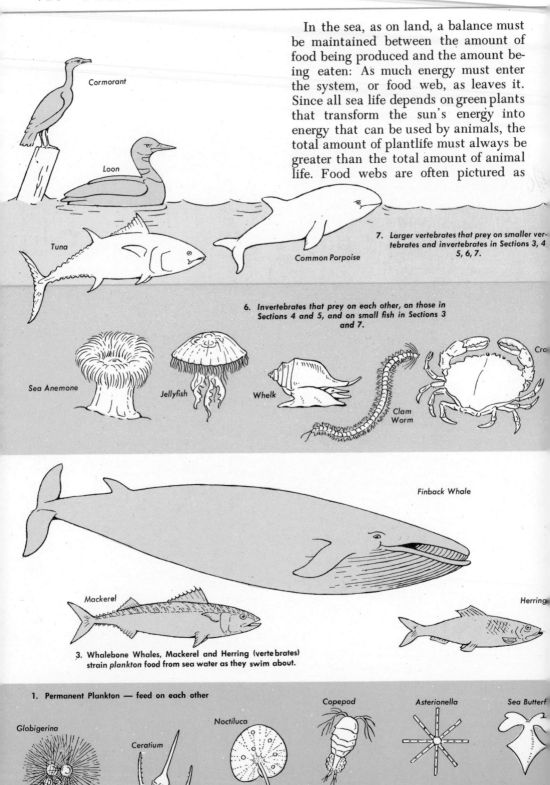

In the sea, as on land, a balance must be maintained between the amount of food being produced and the amount being eaten: As much energy must enter the system, or food web, as leaves it. Since all sea life depends on green plants that transform the sun's energy into energy that can be used by animals, the total amount of plantlife must always be greater than the total amount of animal life. Food webs are often pictured as

Cormorant

Loon

Tuna

Common Porpoise

7. Larger vertebrates that prey on smaller vertebrates and invertebrates in Sections 3, 4 5, 6, 7.

6. Invertebrates that prey on each other, on those in Sections 4 and 5, and on small fish in Sections 3 and 7.

Sea Anemone

Jellyfish

Whelk

Clam Worm

Cra

Finback Whale

Mackerel

Herring

3. Whalebone Whales, Mackerel and Herring (vertebrates) strain plankton food from sea water as they swim about.

1. Permanent Plankton — feed on each other

Globigerina

Ceratium

Noctiluca

Copepod

Asterionella

Sea Butterf

PLANKTON — Drifting Plant and Animal life (Mostly Microscopic) pyramids with a great number of food-producers at the bottom, fewer plant-eaters in the middle, and a few large carnivores at the top. Biologists call this the *pyramid of numbers.* To read the chart below, begin with number one (bottom left) and trace the levels in the sea food web from the tiny plankton to large carnivorous animals. Animals in each of the seven groups have similar feeding habits.

American Eagle

Osprey

Sea Lion

Killer Whale

Harbor Seal

Octopus

Squid

Lobster

Starfish

4. These *plankton*-feeding invertebrates cause sea water to flow through them or to them by means of rapidly beating cilia (hairs) or rapidly beating "feet."

Oyster

Sea Squirt

Barnacle

Sponge

Clam

5. Invertebrates that scrape *plankton* from the area over which or through which they crawl.

Limpet

Sea Cucumber

Periwinkle

Sea Urchin

Diatoms

Diatoma

Synedra

Larva of Hermit Crab

Medusa of Jellyfish

Larva of Sea Urchin

Larva of Edible Crab

2. Plankton only in larval stage — feed on each other and on those in Section 1.

A simple food chain can be illustrated by the interrelationships among organisms in a small pond. The solid arrows point from prey to predator; the dotted arrow indicates the disposal of some waste products or the death of the organism. A= plankton, B= small animals. Bacteria and fungi at work at the bottom of the pond, living on the waste and the dead, return to the waters of the pond the supply of raw materials used by the plants (*see below*)

Actually, the situation is always more complex. Several carnivores feed on other carnivores, and some ecologists make a distinction between first level and second level carnivores. Then, too, many organisms are parasitic and do not play a direct role in the food chain. Each organism has only a limited number of other organisms with which it is linked in an eat-eaten relationship. (*See Balance of Nature; and Wildlife Community*)

—G.A.B.

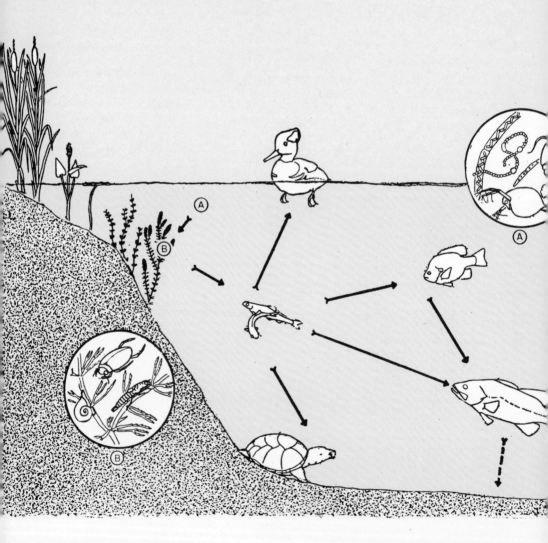

FORAMINIFERA

Of all the living creatures of the earth, only those of the order Foraminifera have contributed significantly to the formation of geological layers. Often called forams, these marine protozoa are visible only under magnification. Most form limy shells within which they live, and these shells sink to the bottom when the animal dies. Some species were so numerous that the dead shells formed huge deposits of lime on the sea floor, where they hardened under pressure into chalk or limestone. Later geologic uplifts often brought these strata above the surface of the water to form plains, cliffs, and even mountains.

Many species of forams are pelagic, drifting with the surface currents of warm seas. Others live on the ocean floor. All of the limy-shelled forams are continually extracting calcium, carbon, and oxygen from seawater, and their shells are accumulating in immeasurably vast layers of ooze under today's oceans. This ooze, in its turn, will become chalk and limestone, rocks formed from the skeletons of living animals.   —G.B.S.

FOREST

The definition of a forest as a tract of land covered with trees is accurate, but the implication that all forests are alike, for that reason, is misleading. A dense tangle of black spruce, deep in glistening snow, at the edge of the tundra in the Northwest Territories of Canada; a mangrove jungle standing on roots that are above a saltwater mud flat along the margin of the Florida Everglades; a thicket of sotol, chittamwood, and cholla in the Chihuahuan Desert: each of these is a forest, though they differ markedly from each other.

Variations in climate, rainfall, soil composition, and exposure to sunlight determine the nature of the trees in any forest, for each species has its own requirements that must be met if it is to survive. Trees with the same needs tend to grow in the same region, with the more efficient trees crowding out those that are less able to compete for life's necessities. Those that customarily grow under the same conditions and in the same areas make up what is called a plant association. An association of trees that tend to be replaced by their own offspring, rather than by other species, is called a climax forest. Over a broad area a set of associations of similar species is called a plant formation, or plant region. North America has nine of these broad regions.

The northern forest region extends southward from the timberline. It is coniferous, composed of spruce and fir and, along its southern border, of jack pine. In lowland areas it crosses the Canadian border into Maine, New York, the Great Lakes region; it follows down the Appalachians to the Great Smokies, and through the Rocky Mountains and the Cascades at high elevations.

The Rocky Mountain forest region has two distinct floras within it. On the higher mountains, just below the timberline, the subalpine forest contains spruce (Engelmann and Colorado blue), alpine fir, limber pine, and bristlecone pine. (*See Arctic-Alpine*). At lower elevations the Gambel oak, white and yellow pines, and Rocky Mountain juniper dominate the montane forest.

The eastern forest region is one of mixed deciduous trees of many species, often subdivided by the major associations within it. Some of these are the beech-maple forest, the maple-basswood forest, the oak-hickory forest, the southern river-bottom forest (cypress and gum trees), and a coniferous group, the southern pines. The region extends from the St. Lawrence River to central Florida and west to the Great Plains.

The western woodland forest region is typical of the Great Basin and is dominated by sagebrush and oaks. In part of its territory it becomes chaparral —dense oak thickets mixed with prickly

Deciduous forest in winter

pear, manzanita, and buck brush.

The Pacific Northwest region has three types of forest. The Pacific lowland forest of coast redwood, giant cedar, Lawson cypress, tan and Garry oaks, and a host of other trees that require a great amount of moisture, flourish in this zone of high precipitation. The Sierran montane forest, along the mountain slopes, has sugar and western yellow pines, oaks, maples, and other deciduous species. At higher elevations, the Sierran subalpine forest contains foxtail, Jeffrey and lodgepole pine, red fir, mountain hemlock, oaks, mountain ash, and mountain lilac.

Deciduous forest in summer

The Caribbean subtropical flora occurs in the United States in extreme southern Florida, with some species spread west along the Gulf Coast to Texas. It includes cabbage and thatch palms, mahogany, wild figs, mastic, stoppers, and mangroves.

As climatic conditions change, the plant associations that are favored by the changes tend to spread, usually at the expense of those that cannot adapt as well to the new conditions. North America has seen many fluctuations in its vegetation, particularly during the Ice Age. The glaciers overwhelmed the northern portion of the

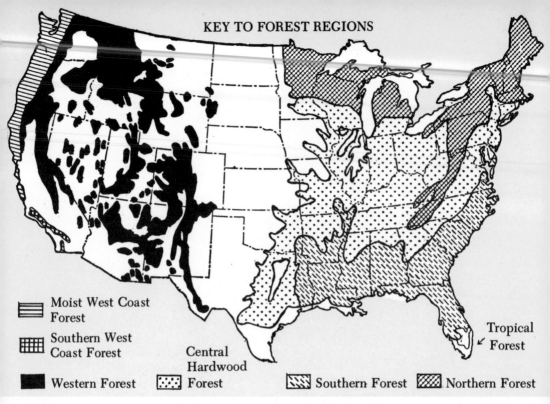

Moist West Coast Forest

Southern West Coast Forest

Western Forest

Central Hardwood Forest

Southern Forest

Northern Forest

Tropical Forest

Major forest regions of the United States

continent, compressing the various floras into more limited territories, and pushing a band of boreal northern region plants before it. With each retreat of the ice, the floras would expand, only to be driven back again. After the last glacier, which retreated about 15,000 years ago, the trees again surged northward to recover lost ground.

Floral regions and associations are named for the largest plants growing within them. Yet in each of these groups there are trees that never grow as large as the dominant ones but that are just as characteristic; others, still smaller, remain shrubs. Sassafras, witch hazel, dogwood, and mountain laurel in the East, and bladdernut, rusty-leaf, and the buckthorns in the West are all in this group. It is possible to divide a forest into about five layers. Each forest, within its region has its typical plants, birds, and mammals. The uppermost layer of the forest is the overstory; then comes the understory layer, the shrub layer, the herb layer, and finally the forest floor. (*See under Animal: Animal Habitats of a Forest*).

Forests have many uses. The most obvious is the lumber that they produce; it has been said that wood is man's second greatest need, second only to food. Forests furnish a host of other products, including nuts, gums, resins, medicinals, dyes, and raw materials for paper and certain chemical industries.

The decaying leaves, twigs, and branches form humus on the forest floor, organic matter that can be assimilated by living trees and that builds up the soil in volume and in quality. Forests protect watersheds from erosion by slowing down the flow of runoff water and by shielding the soil from the impact of heavy rains. They are the homes for much of the continent's wildlife. Their value to human recreation is being recognized more and more.

The forests of North America are continually changing. Where once they covered more than 40 percent of the United States and about the same of Canada, lumbering exhausted much of the East of its most valuable woods and the most accessible of the western forests are also gone. For almost 300 years of human history on this continent, no attempt was made to replant. Early in the 20th Century the annual lumber crop actually exceeded the amount of replacement. Since then, silviculturists and exponents of practical forest management, developed the concept of sustained yield in forest cutting and reforestation. In practice this means that a cutover area is reseeded to valuable species, or a nearby natural stand is left for natural reseeding, or the cutting is done selectively to leave maturing trees and seedlings for future harvesting. (*See under Tree*)   —G.B.S.

Recommended Reading

Forest and the Sea—Marston Bates. Random House, Inc., New York.
The Perpetual Forest—W.B. Collins. J.B. Lippincott Company, Philadelphia.
The Tropical Rain Forest: An Ecological Study—P.W. Richards. Cambridge University Press, New York.

Forests and Wildlife

National forests have been established in the North, South, East and West— these belong to every citizen of the United States, and are enjoyed by thousands of people throughout the year. They are an important economic resource, they play a strategic role in water and soil conservation, and they form a vast reservoir of wildlife.

More than half a century ago, when the conservation movement was getting under way, the forest lands were among the first withdrawn from the public domain to be protected and managed for the benefit of the people. Although the production of timber and management of watersheds were primary concerns, the United States Forest Service immediately became aware of its responsibility toward wildlife. In those early days, the task was principally one of protection.

Map of the United States showing location of national forests (solid areas) and purchase units (shaded areas)

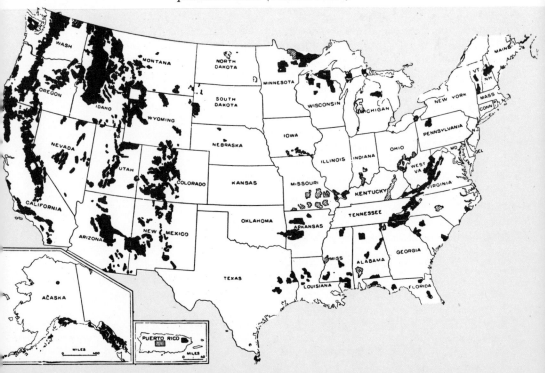

The depletion of wildlife in the national forests was part of a general condition. In the West particularly, the early settlers believed that there was an inexhaustible supply of fish and game. This attitude, plus the fact that game laws either did not exist or provided little control over the take of fish and game, led to the overharvesting of wildlife resources. Forty years ago state fish and game departments were few and, where they did exist, were underfinanced and poorly manned.

Concurrent with the settlement and development of much of the agricultural and range land in and adjacent to the national forest areas, there was brought about a partial or complete adjustment in the home territories of much of the wildlife. Valleys that had been available to deer, elk, birds, and other animals were fenced and placed under cultivation or put to other uses that tended to exclude the species formerly roaming these areas at will. Moreover, the development of roads and railroads, along with the growth of towns and cities, tended to upset the wildlife environment.

The establishment of national forests was fortunate for some forms of wildlife, in that wild areas were provided in which many species could find the isolation and protection they needed. In this respect, relic groups of elk, grizzly bear, bighorn sheep, beaver, grouse, ptarmigan, and many other species persisted in isolated portions of the national forests after their kind had been exterminated from much of their natural range.

About the turn of the century, conservationists began to acquaint the public with the need for protection and restoration of North American big game. These campaigns demonstrated that many species—formerly abundant—had been reduced to a few colonies. As the facts became known, the state legislatures rose to the rescue of wildlife by passing restrictive laws and, in many cases, actually closed the season for indefinite periods. Some of these closures have remained in effect since their initiation over a generation ago. The general trend, however, once the seriousness of the situation was realized, was to provide for short hunting seasons and small bag limits.

Throughout this period of protection and restoration, the United States Forest Service was active in furthering the welfare of wildlife on national forest lands. Forest officers aided in enforcing state game laws and in bringing game violators to court. The United States Forest Service, the state game departments, and local game associations also cooperated in introducing elk in our national forest areas where they had been exterminated. Thus many herds were started which now provide fine hunting for thousands of sportsmen. Somewhat later, deer and turkeys were released on many national forests in the eastern and southern United States to repopulate lands they had once occupied. Throughout the national forests, the limited population of beaver was given protection and also distributed to new territories through an active program of live trapping (*See under Beaver*). Fish resources were considerably expanded by stocking streams and lakes.

Along with the efforts to increase wildlife through protection and restocking, there was a strong movement to establish federal and state refuges. Many such refuges were set up in national forests.

Emphasis on protection and restoration was necessary if reasonably adequate numbers were to be attained. However, neither the United States Forest Service, the states, nor the general public were quite prepared for the phenomenal success of the program, especially in the rapid multiplication of such species as deer, elk, beaver, antelope, and black bear.

The first real indication of the danger of overpopulation of deer came to light on the Kaibab National Forest. Here a mule deer herd was overprotected by the killing off of most of the cougars and wolves that kept the mule deer herd within the bounds of its natural food supply. The herd prospered until it reached an estimated size of 100,000. Forage resources were inadequate and within three years (1924–1926) the herd was reduced by starvation, disease, and other natural causes to less than 10,000. The range was so severely damaged, however, that twenty years after the die-off it was still considered advisable to keep the number down to about 15,000. Since this shocking episode, similar losses have occurred throughout North America. Unfortunately, many of these problems have developed on national forest lands, and food resources for wildlife have been so damaged that only a fraction of the herds can now be maintained on a sound management basis.

The unsatisfactory big game conditions have focused attention of conser-

Poor growth of a coniferous forest (above) is improved by controlled thinning (below). The pictures were taken five years apart

vationists on the need for adjusting herds to the normal food resources. Consequently, game authorities are now thinking in terms of management and utilization as contrasted to protection and restoration. Attention is given to determining the sizes of the herds, condition of the ranges, and appropriate hunter take. This is being brought about through state action to open refuges, lengthen hunting seasons, and provide for the taking of female animals, where conditions warrant.

The United States Forest Service works closely with state game departments in furthering desirable objectives of game management on national forest lands. Annual estimates are made of animal populations, and sometimes actual counts are taken on the winter range, either by ground crews or from airplanes. Checks are commonly made of the hunter take to obtain information on the number, condition of the animals, and place of kill. Special attention is given to surveys of forage conditions to determine whether the range is being properly cropped, and whether its productivity is favorably or unfavorably affected by wildlife.

In many instances, the United States Forest Service has provided a suitable environment for rare or vanishing species. In this connection, the California condor immediately comes to mind. This great bird is now largely confined to Los Padres National Forest, where it finds the isolation and rugged terrain that seems essential to its preservation and successful nesting. To further protect the condor, the United States Forest Service has established a sanctuary about the Sisquoc Falls nesting area, closed to public use.

The welfare of the condor is of special concern to the National Audubon Society, which has encouraged protective measures such as the Sisquoc Sanctuary and has undertaken studies, notably those by Carl Koford, to learn more about the bird's habits as a means of proposing further action for its protection and restoration (*See Condor*).

In the administration of the national forests, the United States Forest Service has several major responsibilities. First there is the all-important matter of safeguarding the resources. This includes fire suppression, since fire can be a terribly destructive enemy of the forest and its inhabitants.

Along with protection is the day-to-day job of administering the national forests. The cutting of timber and grazing of livestock must be so conducted that the productivity of the land is not impaired. Moreover, the many demands for the use of the land must be regulated so that neither destruction of the plant cover or soil is permitted, nor conflicts for the products or services of a single area of land allowed to develop. Where the land is extremely valuable for a single use, however, it may be in the public interest to recognize such a situation and reduce or eliminate the conflicting demands. Under this principle the United States Forest Service has designated roadless areas, wilderness areas, and other territories where recreational use or preservation of natural conditions is the main concern.

Wildlife of some kind will find a home regardless of the character of the plant cover or the use the land is subjected to. Moreover, it often happens that the removal of forest products is actually beneficial to many species. Properly managed cutting of timber, for example, opens the forest and encourages the growth of plants that in turn provide food and cover for deer, turkey, grouse, and many other species. More and more attention is being given to leaving suitable trees to provide dens for squirrels, raccoons, and other animals, and to produce fruits, berries, and mast for them to eat. There is still much to be done, but the increased recognition being given the place of wildlife in the national forests is indicative of the benefits that lie ahead.   —L.W.S.

FOREST INSECTS (*See under Insect Control*)

FOSSIL

A relic of the life of past ages, recovered from beneath the surface of the earth or sea, a fossil may be a completely preserved animal or plant, a portion or a product of either, or an impression of what was once a living entity. A fossil is a visible trace of some organism that lived in the geological past; the study of fossils is the fundamental basis of the science of *paleontology*, or the study of ancient life. Fossil, from the Latin, originally meant anything that had been dug up; today the word applies only to something that was once alive or has resulted from life processes.

The degree of fossilization of an animal or plant varies with the circumstances at the time of its demise and the subsequent history of its remains. When quick freezing, immersion in oil, or embedding in amber (fossilized resin) was involved, all of the animal or plant may have been preserved intact. Generally, soft animal parts decay, leaving only the bones or the shell; plant tissues break down into carbon. The structures may be preserved without change, or they may be completely replaced by other chemicals while the original form is maintained, as in the silica replacement of wood in eastern Arizona's Petrified Forest National Monument and in the calcium carbonate replacement of bone in most dinosaur skeletons. Seashells and the chitinous parts of insects and worms are seldom chemically altered. Casts, or impressions, of long-dead forms often indicate their original size, shape, and external texture; tracks may reveal something of the habits of the animal that made them.

Almost everything we know of earlier forms of life has been based on fossil evidence. The mastodons, dinosaurs, trilobites, giant lycopods, seed ferns,

Fossil, or petrified wood is formed when silica dissolved in water replaces the cellular structure of tree trunks

and a host of other life forms are represented on the earth of today only by their fossils, although some were related to very different creatures that have survived or evolved from them. The theory of evolution was formulated, in part, to explain fossils, and still derives much of its support from them.

Fossils are helpful in studying the history of life on earth and in dating the age of geological events. The approximate age of many different kinds of fossils has been carefully calculated and catalogued, and the presence of one of these *index fossils* is a clue to the age of the geological beds in which it is found. Various kinds of small sea animals—for example, foraminifers (*see under Foraminifera*)—have been so carefully studied, and the differences between species and subspecies made so distinct that, used as index fossils, many geological deposits can be dated as to whether they are early or late in a given period. Fossils also indicate which areas of the earth's surface were under seas, or were deserts, swamps, or tropical forests at a particular time in the earth's long history.   —G.B.S.

Recommended Reading

Fossil Book: A Record of Prehistoric Life— Carroll L. and Mildred A. Fenton. Doubleday & Company, Inc. Garden City, New York.
Fossil Crustacea of the Atlantic and Gulf Coastal Plain—M. J. Rathbun. Geological Society of America, Inc. New York.
Fossil Evidence for Human Evolution—W. E. Le Gros Clark. University of Chicago Press.
Fossils: Introduction to Prehistoric Life—W. H. Matthews. Barnes & Noble, Inc. New York.
Fossils in America—Jay E. Ransom. Harper & Row, Inc. New York.

FOX

Gray Fox

Other Common Names—Woods fox, tree fox

Scientific Name—*Urocyon cinereoargenteus*

Family—Canidae (dog family)

Order—Carnivora

Size—Body length, 21 to 29 inches; tail 11 to 16 inches; weight, 7 to 13 pounds

Range—Eastern and southern United States; New Hampshire west to northeastern North Dakota south to Florida Keys and entire Gulf Coast; also south from Colorado, Utah, and southwestern Washington to southern Baja California, Mexico, and northern South America

Habits of the Gray Fox

One of the most interesting mammals of the United States is the little gray, or woods, fox. It usually lives in swamps, woodlands, and chaparral, or in the cactus and mesquite thickets of the dry deserts. It is shy and secretive, smaller than its bolder cousin, the red fox, which lives more on open farmland.

The gray fox is the only fox that is apt to climb trees, and it preys on a large number of small mammals—rabbits, wood rats, ground squirrels, mice, gophers, tree squirrels, and hares. It also eats wild birds, turtles and their eggs, snakes, grapes, wild cherries, and other fruits, and carrion of all kinds.

For all its cunning, the gray fox has a short lifespan. The life-expectancy of the average newborn fox is a mere 11 months, and those fortunate enough to escape premature fate at the hands of their only important enemy—people— live an average of only a year and a half. What saves the gray fox from near oblivion is its astounding fertility. More than 90 percent of the mature females produce litters in their *first* breeding season, and these litters average more than four pups each. Thus 50 pairs of gray foxes may produce some 225 pups each spring.

These and other facts of fox lore have been compiled through one of the most exhaustive scientific studies ever undertaken of the North American gray fox. For five years, John E. Wood of Jacksonville University, Jacksonville, Florida, and David E. Davis of Johns Hopkins University, Baltimore, assisted by Rexford Lord, carried out a field study of the fox populations in Georgia, Flor-

The gray fox dwells where there is cover and seldom lives more than eighteen months

ida, and South Carolina.

The primary purpose of the study was to provide information that would aid in the control of rabies. The important question was to determine the preval-ence of rabies virus in foxes, and to determine the role of fox populations in epidemics of rabies in the southeastern United States.

Wood and Davis selected Thomas-

Ninety percent of mature female gray foxes bear young the first breeding season. Most litters average more than four pups

ville, Georgia, as their headquarters. The plantlife of that area is representative of a wide belt of typical vegetation extending in a broad arc from Virginia across northern Florida to Texas. Significantly, the incidence of rabies is noticeably higher in the overgrown fields with good natural food supply making up much of this selected study area than it is in more agriculturally developed sections.

It has long been known that the fox population is a prime carrier of rabies virus. Of the 1,026 gray foxes the researchers trapped, 3.1 percent were found to be infected with rabies virus. Rabies from the bite of an infected gray fox is not numerically serious to humans. Only one or two persons per state per year are bitten by rabid animals, and the Pasteur treatment, though arduous, is effective if used early. It is in the matter of livestock infection that fox-carried rabies becomes more of a threat. A single rabid fox has been known to infect 20 cows in one brief rampage.

Though the study was primarily one of fox population factors and rabies incidence, the researchers enriched fox lore considerably. Davis pointed out that the fox is possibly the only animal species with a really cohesive family life. Adult gray foxes are mated until the death of a partner. After the pups are born each March, the family aggregation stays together through the entire summer—an extremely long time for a wild animal. Young woodchucks, for example, disperse in July. Skunks leave their mothers in late summer. Beavers stay together until the next young are born, but their society is more of a communal affair than one of defined families. Long after the young of most wild animals are on their own, the fox pup is still very much a part of the family group.

Because fox families remain together for this unusually long period, the young pups receive perhaps the most extensive training of any animal in the wild. The skilled kingfisher, by example, teaches its young the facts of foraging for 10 days or so; the woodchuck for several weeks. Young foxes undergo a full four-month training course under the watchful eyes of both parents, and particularly the vixen. She teaches her pups in great detail how to catch grasshoppers, mice, and other preferred items, and she is known to instruct through patient and repeated demonstration. When a young fox graduates from this rigid course, it is fully prepared to strike out on its own.

Contrary to popular belief, the fox is far from being a dedicated killer of poultry. It takes whatever food is easiest to come by, and its preferred animal staple is field mice. Wood and Davis discovered that rabbits, rodents and small birds represented about half of the annual diet of the gray foxes they studied. The balance was made up of insects—mainly grasshoppers—and peanuts, persimmons, and plums, plus, of course, minor quantities of other wild foods. The gray fox attacks the chicken yard only when an unwary farmer exposes his fowl.

The gray fox is no wanderer. Many of them captured during the study were tattooed with code numbers on the ear and released. Fifty-six of these were later recaptured, and more than half of them had not traveled as much as a mile in three months. This led to the conclusion that the fox population in any given area has a high birthrate and a high death rate, and the emigration is at a minimum.

Because the five-year study was dedicated to the improvement of rabies control, one's first thought is why not virtually eliminate the fox? If it is a prime carrier of rabies, then its extermination should go a long way toward controlling the disease. With the fox's lack of wanderlust, one's first impression is that control of the fox should be easy.

Even if there were a way to com-

Swift fox from Audubon's Elephant Folio

pletely exterminate foxes and the cost was trivial, one must keep in mind that the fox is an integral part of ecology. If it were eliminated, a chain of unpredictable events would be set in motion. For example, the fox is a major factor in holding down the cotton rat population in the southeastern states. With foxes gone, the number of cotton rats could soar. One of the favorite foods of cotton rats is quail eggs. Elimination of the fox might quickly lead to drastic reduction of the quail population, which would be just one immediate effect.

Hopefully, drastic control measures of gray foxes do not appear necessary. The fox population and its accompanying incidence of rabies coincides with changes in the agricultural use of the land. In the 1930's and 1940's, as cotton fields were abandoned and permitted to revert to excellent overgrown wild cover, the gray fox increased and so did cases of rabies. But throughout the southern states, there has been a marked shift to pulpwood tree farming and to pastureland. As more and more abandoned acreage is cleared and converted into tree farms and pasture, gray foxes face a dwindling food supply and their numbers decrease as a natural consequence.

In spite of the quick panic aroused by an occasional rabid fox, the study has shown the fox to be an integral, interesting, and ecologically necessary member of the North American fauna.

—W.H.

Kit and Swift Foxes

The beautiful little North American foxes of our western deserts and plains, known as kit and swift foxes, are chiefly nocturnal in their habits and are therefore seldom seen. Although the English names are sometimes used indiscriminately, the name swift fox, *Vulpes velox*, generally refers to the animal of the plains, which has a more northern and eastern range. Kit fox, *Vulpes macrotis*, is the fox inhabiting the southwestern deserts; because of its environment, the kit fox is often referred to as the desert fox. In color both foxes are a buff-yellow, the kit fox tending to be of a lighter hue.

The swift fox is slightly larger in size. The main distinction between the two, however, is the greater size of the kit fox's ears, which measure about 3¾ inches. In contrast the ears of the swift fox are just over 3 inches.

The range of the swift fox formerly extended throughout most of the North American plains from southern Alberta, Saskatchewan, and Manitoba south to northern Texas and eastern New Mexico, while that of the kit fox was from southern Oregon and Idaho south through Baja California and into northern Mexico. Over much of this territory these foxes are either becoming rare or have been exterminated.

Both foxes make their homes in burrows, which are either dug by the foxes themselves or are made in excavations of other animals. Besides the home den, other burrows are utilized. The home burrow generally has one or more exits. The young are born in the spring and usually number from four to seven. Both parents share in the care of the cubs.

The kit and swift foxes are fleet of foot and are accomplished dodgers, but they cannot sustain their speed for long; if pursued, sooner or later they must rely upon going underground to escape. Thus it is very advantageous to have various burrows around a large area. Besides man, there are a few other enemies. Eagles, coyotes, and wolves all prey upon these foxes.

Small rodents and insects appear to be the main diet of the kit and swift foxes, but rabbits, birds and their eggs, reptiles, and some vegetable matter are also eaten. The stomach of one swift fox that was examined held nothing but grasshoppers. The larger kangaroo rats, when they are obtainable, seem to be one of the main sources of food for the kit fox. One of the surest ways to determine whether any of these foxes are in an area is to look for their footprints among the burrows of a colony of these rodents.

There are two forms of the swift fox.

The northern race, which lives north of northern Nebraska, is slightly larger and grayer than the southern form. The kit fox has been divided into eight races, differing slightly in size and color. Some scientists believe that it may yet be proved that both of these belong to the same species.

It is deplorable that these small foxes, which are destroyers of rodents and insects and are therefore useful to mankind, are killed off because of man's warfare against other carnivores. Swift foxes and kit foxes lack the cunning of the larger foxes, coyotes, and wolves and are thus easily trapped. They will take a poison bait that a craftier animal would readily shun. Systematically poisoning a valley can deplete the region of all the small foxes, while only a few of the less cunning of the coyotes will be taken.

In former years these foxes had a very extensive range but it is being greatly reduced. Agriculture and livestock and all their complications are too big a competition for these little foxes. It is only in regions unsuited for man's needs that the swift and kit foxes will probably survive.   —T.D.C.

Kit Fox
Other Common Names—Desert fox
Scientific Name—*Vulpes macrotis*
Family—Canidae (dog family)
Order—Carnivora
Size—Body length, 24 to 31 inches; tail, 9 to 12 inches; weight, 3 to 6 pounds
Range—A desert dweller. Southwestern United States, south to northern Mexico and Baja California; north to southern and central California

Swift Fox
Other Common Names—None
Scientific Name—*Vulpes velox*
Family—Canidae (dog family)
Order—Carnivora
Size—Essentially same as kit fox

Range—Central United States, north to Saskatchewan and Alberta, south through eastern Montana, Wyoming, northern and eastern Colorado, North and South Dakota, Nebraska, western Kansas, eastern New Mexico, western Texas and Oklahoma

Red Fox
Other Common Names—Colored fox
Scientific Name—*Vulpes fulva*
Family—Canidae (dog family)
Order—Carnivora
Size—Body length, 36 to 42 inches; tail, 13 to 15 inches; weight, 6 to 15 pounds
Range—All North America except the southern Atlantic and Gulf coast regions, southern Great Plains, southwestern deserts, and Pacific Coast

Habits of the Red Fox

During the 35 years or so that foxes regularly have been part of one's life, he may have seen enough to make him careful about discounting the stories of red fox exploits. After allowing for exaggerations, faulty or questionable interpretations, and the role of chance in the events described, a substantial residuum could still be truth, or close to it. The red fox is a species that can show unusual intelligence. As concerns the behavior of an individual fox, it may not be safe to say that anything can happen, but some remarkable things are possible.

The foxes of Minnesota, Wisconsin, Iowa, and South Dakota, are subspecies of red and gray foxes. Red and gray foxes are animals of somewhat different habitats. In this region, rocky hills comprise typical strongholds for the grays, but grays are occasionally found far out on the prairies. Conversely, the red foxes prefer open land but may also be found in the forest. Indeed, at times evidence has been reported of what could be severe competition between the two, with one species or the other increasing as the other species declines.

Gray foxes are not among the really "foxy" foxes. They do not look like what many think of as foxes. Even their tracks in the snow may seem more catlike than foxlike. They spend much time in holes—under ledges and bluffs—whereas the reds hardly enter holes at all except when they have young in the dens. The grays also have tree-climbing abilities, tendencies toward gregariousness in winter, and other attributes not usually associated with northern-states red foxes (*See Gray Fox*).

Experience does not suggest that differences in appearance and behavior between red and gray foxes make the gray foxes any less genuine as wild animals. The grays are adapted for a way of life and are interesting, in themselves, as part of the outdoors. It is simply that a fox is a *red fox* to those people to whom the word *fox* arouses a special mental image in red and yellow, an image of a bushy tail almost as big as its possessor's body, of a certain creature bounding across a field or lying asleep on a sunny hillside or bedded down in a smartweed patch or on a snowdrift, or of the maker of straight-line tracks about a marsh or along a cattle trail. It is of red fox that one thinks in connection with fox hounds, sour grapes, and shenanigans in chicken yards.

In popular thought, the red fox has become the embodiment of cunning and mischief. It does have its playfulness—as do many other dogs, wild or tame, and many other animals that do not belong to the dog family. One need not be surprised because fox puppies romp, toss objects in the air, engage in mock fights, or do something else that they obviously want to.

People must not, in any realistic appraisal of fox behavior, ignore individual differences. Ordinary red foxes may not show a great deal of originality, either in taking care of themselves or in their hunting. To many of the problems of living, they do not have particularly effective answers. Although they may easily avoid the traps spread over the

countryside by unguided amateur trappers, professionals may trap them by the dozens in a single winter by means of a limited number of effective trap "sets."
Field researches have repeatedly demonstrated how well-suited populations of bobwhite quail and muskrats—two prey species toward which the foxes may show favoritism when they can catch them—may get along for months at a time without losses to foxes, the presence and efforts of high fox populations in their vicinity, notwithstanding. Most of the hunting by red foxes seems to be about as unimaginative and routine as hunting by the general run of hawks, owls, weasels, and other predators that may have decidedly lower learning capacities than the foxes. To all of these predators, *availability* of their prey is the main factor governing what they prey upon and how much. But, once in a while, an observer may witness the sort of intelligent behavior or "specialization" that gives foxes their reputation for foxiness.

It is often possible to learn much about an individual red fox on the basis of *sign* (trails, uneaten food remains, feces, etc.). Resident adult foxes confine most of their activities to an area having a radius of about a mile. Their activities within this region vary with the time of the year, social relations with other foxes, the presence or absence of formidable enemies, and the food supply. Home ranges of fox families may overlap, but the centers of activity are usually well separated. Strange foxes may be tolerated by the resident foxes or they may be driven off, another instance of the essentially doglike behavior of foxes.

In the northern United States, young red foxes are born in March or early April. The mother may select as prospective denning sites old woodchuck or badger holes or parts of some complicated sets of holes in a rocky hilltop used by generations of burrowing animals of small to medium sizes. These,

she may rehabilitate many weeks before the birth of the young, which first emerge from the den holes when three or four weeks of age.

As the young grow, the ground about the den openings becomes packed, and trails radiate away into surrounding vegetation. Prey remains may or may not be strewn in the vicinity—depending upon the nature of the terrain, the length of time a den may have been occupied, the demands of the young foxes, how good or poor the hunting may be, the types of prey brought in by the adult foxes, the weather, and how much the den sites may be worked over by scavengers. Feathers—easily detached from the bodies of birds that foxes have eaten—tend to be conspicuous out of proportion to the birds actually occurring in fox diets.

The delectable meadow mice are usually so well cleaned up that about the only evidence of them at a den may be in the fox droppings. Sometimes, considerable numbers of the whole bodies of the less-preferred white-footed mice and harvest mice may be found, sometimes in heaps. Foxes may kill weasels, moles, and shrews as they meet them, and they often leave them uneaten at the dens or along their trails. Young foxes may play with the mummified carcasses of these victims, but it seems to take a very hungry fox to eat anything so patently ill-flavored.

If the foxes have access to much farm carrion of transportable sizes—dead poultry or small pigs spread over fields with manure, or even a stillborn calf or the leg bone of a horse or cow—this carrion may show up at fox dens. Miscellaneous den debris may include sticks, dry livestock dung, and old bones used for playthings.

Early in the rearing season, den sites are commonly changed after a few weeks, then more frequently as the pups grow larger and more active. The new den may be within a hundred yards of the one being vacated or up to a half

The red fox feeds mainly on small rodents and carrion

mile or more away. Of course, what the foxes do both reflects the alternatives open to them and the necessity of moving. Moves that are not forced outright by emergencies or the threat of danger appear to be due principally to foxes wanting to get away from a befouled den or away from one that is proving to be too wet or otherwise uncomfortable.

In midsummer, old den sites may be among the rallying (meeting) stations

for a family of foxes. Hunting as a family group may continue into late summer. These associations doubtless have much value for the young foxes while they are learning to find their own food and picking up the elementary fox "traditions" concerning man and his dogs.

Late summer is a time when foxes may eat roasting ears (ears of sweet corn) in the fields, or fill up on fallen plums, or gorge on grasshoppers and crickets. The staple or much-eaten prey of foxes—the young of all mammals and birds taken regularly—reaches its annual peak of abundance, and hungry young foxes can bungle their hunting repeatedly and still have more opportunities.

By early fall, the young red foxes are on their own and family "sign," as such, may no longer be identified. The information from marked (ear-tagged) foxes suggests that the independent young move well out of the home ranges of their parents. The parent foxes maintain their "old homesteads" and comprise the most nearly permanent fox population of an area; they are, in particular, the individuals that make it their business to know what is what and where is where. The social intolerances of the red fox seldom permit these "vested interest" populations to exceed a pair per square mile in the wild. Transients drifting through or discreetly hanging about the outskirts of defended territories (or trespassing when they can get away with it) may temporarily raise local fox concentrations in habitats attractive to them because of abundant food and cover.

As is generally the case with mammals and birds, the less attached foxes, or "drifters," are the ones that have the least chance to reproduce successfully and the biggest chance of having tragedies befall them. They are typically the overproduced young of the past breeding season and, in naturally self-limiting population systems, the ones that are fundamentally expendable. Naturally, too, they do their best to stay alive, to do something with themselves, even in places where there is neither food enough nor room enough for them and where they know that they are unwanted. In time, maybe, a member of an established pair may become very old or ailing or be killed, and an upstart youngster may replace it, thereby advancing itself in the red fox society.

In the matter of daily eating, the foxes, along with other opportunistic predators, may be expected to catch vulnerable prey animals as they meet them. These victims—rabbits, quail, pheasants, and other small animals—may be handicapped because of immaturity, illness, or injuries—notably, those crippled by gunshot during hunting seasons. A large proportion of victims fall in the category of parts of populations that exceed the capacity of the environment to accommodate them—the individuals that are too preoccupied with fighting or bickering among themselves to attend to the business of staying alive or those circulating restlessly in strange places or in the poorer grades of living quarters. Or the victims may be vulnerable to predation because an ice storm or a heavy snowfall has starved out a quail population, or the refuge cover of a marsh or weed patch or woodlot has been destroyed by fire, or something else has gone overwhelmingly wrong for the species preyed upon.

At times of exceptional availability of prey, the foxes make caches of uneaten material, which is sometimes buried under dirt, snow, or vegetation, or sometimes left lying about. People occasionally come to winter caches of foxes containing mice or rabbits that the foxes may visit from time to time, whether they eat of them or not. The caches are fox "property"—as may also be miscellaneous prospective food items claimed by them, including carcasses of animals that the foxes had no part in killing.

Red foxes in the Midwest have a propensity for biting off and swallowing the frozen feet of carcasses of chickens, pheasants, coots, ducks, muskrats, even if they do not eat more of them. They may vary this habit by biting off the easily detachable heads of these animals and, in the case of muskrats, the frozen tails.

This caching unquestionably has advantages as a survival trait for foxes. During periods of easy hunting, the foxes may seldom need to resort to stored food, but, when the hunting is difficult, the caches may still have something that is edible—provided that it has not spoiled beyond use of foxes or that crows, minks, skunks, mice, shrews, opossums, raccoons, dogs, or foxes other than the "owners" have not already cleaned it up too thoroughly. Foxes can starve to death, not only in northern wildernesses at times of food shortages but even, though rarely, in the more food-rich parts of fox range. When hunting is poor, there may be something dead lying next to a highway or out in a farmer's stubble field. A genuinely hungry fox is neither proud nor overly fussy about what it eats.

The fact that foxes capture and eat what man wishes to protect may, at times, justify human intervention—merely because it may be to man's advantage to prevent the foxes from doing certain things that would be perfectly natural for them to do. Defining exactly what is to man's advantage may, on the other hand, be quite a job.

The fox predation that man becomes aroused about is chiefly upon poultry or game. Depredations upon poultry can be expensive for the poultryman, but approved practices in poultry husbandry —such as keeping the flocks in enclosures—are automatic safeguards against most losses from foxes. The old farm standby, a good dog, can also be one of the best insurances against foxes taking liberties about a farmyard. As concerns foxes and game, their relations may be complex and easily misunderstood, differing with the locality and the situation.

In Iowa, foxes are particularly blamed by sportsmen for shortages of ring-necked pheasants, bobwhite quail, and cottontail rabbits. That foxes may eat pheasants, quail, or cottontails should soon become apparent to anyone who pays attention to the food habits of foxes living in areas in which pheasants, quail, or cottontails are available as fox food. At least the cottontails may be staple prey of foxes in "cottontail counties."

From the evidence boiled down, one may see that abundant populations of foxes are by no means incompatible with abundant populations of all three of these favorite Iowa game species. Some of the most thriving populations of pheasants, quail, and cottontails are maintained despite large numbers of foxes and other wild predators and despite human hunting pressure. But these thriving game populations all had in common the tremendous advantage of suitable environment in which to live and to reproduce their kinds. In environment that is deficient in its necessities for pheasants, quail, and cottontails, these species do not thrive; furthermore, they stand by for the least chance of coping with predators and with inanimate dangers, alike.

The usual reasoning of the outdoor public is that if the foxes are going to eat so many pheasants, quail, or cottontails, then, if man got rid of the foxes before they killed those pheasants, quail, or cottontails, he should have that much more game—or, at any rate, decidedly more game—awaiting the hunting season. As reasoning, it provides comfortable and satisfying panaceas, but it has an often overlooked factual disadvantage in that this is not the way things are apt to work out. The truth is that a great deal of the predation suffered by wild mammals and birds in Iowa and neighboring states has little effect on the populations maintained by them even when the predation is heavy. The reason for this paradox is this: The young that are annually overproduced in relation to the available habitat are candidates for elimination either through predation or something else. Nature's resiliences and nature's shaking down of wild populations to fit their habitats make ineffectual much human effort intended in behalf of favorite species unless that effort results in bona fide improvements of the habitat for game. (And, even then, weather and other factors must be considered.) On the basis of wildlife investigations carried on over the continent during the past decades, it is doubtful that persecution of foxes or of any native predators could substitute for livable habitat in the management, say, of cottontails as game.   —P.L.E.

Recommended Reading

American Wolves, Coyotes, and Foxes—B. S. Beebe. David Mckay Company, Inc., New York.
Following Fox Trails—Adolph Murie. University of Michigan Press, Museum of Zoology miscellaneous publication No. 32, Ann Arbor, Michigan.
The Red Fox: Friend or Foe—Donald W. Douglass & G. W. Bradt. Game Division, Michigan Department of Conservation, Lansing, Michigan.
Red Foxes and a Declining Prey Population—Thomas G. Scott and Willard D. Klimstra. Southern Illinois University Press, Carbondale, Illinois.
Red Foxes of Michigan—David A. Arnold. Michigan Department of Conservation, Lansing, Michigan.

FRIGATE-BIRD
Magnificent Frigate-bird
Other Common Names—Man-o'-war, man-o'-war hawk
Scientific Name—*Fregata magnificens*
Family—Fregatidae (frigate-birds)
Order—Pelecaniformes
Size—Length, 40 inches
Range—Caribbean, Cape Verdes, Galapagos; in North America, from South Florida west along the Gulf of Mexico

Pirates of the air, living on fishes and other marine animals stolen from gulls, terns, and boobies, the graceful frigate birds are the swiftest flyers of all seabirds. The wings span more than seven feet, yet the body weighs only three or four pounds. They prefer to glide through the air or to hang motionless in the breeze, but their speed in diving or in pursuit of prey is faster than that of any of their victims.

Although related to the pelicans, frigate-birds have lost most of the webbing between the toes. They do not swim

Magnificent frigate-bird

and they avoid landing in the water. The legs are short, the feet small; they cannot run to launch themselves, and the long, gliding wings have scarcely enough initial lift to carry the birds up from a level surface. They must alight on a perch above the water, to gain gliding speed by diving into the wind. The tail, used in steering, can be folded like a sword or spread like a pair of scissors.

The long, thin, hooked beak is sometimes used to pick up food from the surface. The bird swoops downward with considerable speed, levels off close to the surface, then snaps the head downward while in full flight.

The male is black at a distance, faintly tinged with brown and with green iridescence on the back when seen close at hand. He has an inflatable throat pouch, orange or red, used in courtship. The female lacks the pouch, and is white on the breast. Young birds have white heads.

This species does not nest in the United States. It breeds on uninhabited islands in the Bahamas, the West Indies, and northern South America. Although primarily coastal, it is often found far out at sea.   —G.B.S.

FROG

In common usage, the word frog is often applied indiscriminately to a great many members of the order Salienta—the tailless amphibia. Strictly and scientifically speaking, however, only members of the family Ranidae can be called true frogs. In general, the principal visual features they hold in common are a streamlined body; a moist and smooth skin; long, slender legs that enable them to make enormous leaps; webbed toes on their hind legs that make them excellent swimmers, even though some of them may be found quite far from water; large eardrums; and protruding eyes. The males of most true frogs have paired vocal pouches located at the sides of their throats, and these pouches enable them to utter grunting, croaking, or plunking sounds.

Like most Salienta, frogs lay their eggs in the water where they are externally fertilized by sperms ejected over them by the male. The eggs, engulfed in a gelatinous mass, may be found either floating netlike on the surface of the water, as are the eggs of the bullfrog and the green frog, or in clusters attached to submerged branches, as are the eggs of the wood frog. The time of development from egg to mature frog depends not only on the individual species, but also on temperature and other climatic conditions. Almost all young frogs complete their metamorphosis to adulthood within one year, but the bullfrog spends two winters as a tadpole.

Frogs feed exclusively on living creatures, although any moving object may be mistaken by them for food and readily seized by a flip of the tongue, the front of which is attached to the tip of the lower jaw while the back end lies loose, ready to be flung forward. Voracious eaters, frogs are preyed upon by many creatures including their own kind and by man himself.

In captivity, aquatic frogs should be kept in an aquarium that contains a rock or other solid ground, upon which the frog can sit above water. Semiaquatic, or terrestrial, frogs, such as the wood frog, should be kept in a moist terrarium planted with mosses; the terrarium must also contain a shallow water dish in which the frog may bathe, as well as a plant or small cave to provide shade. Earthworms and insects may be offered as food; small bits of lean meat are accepted by them if moved to resemble a living creature.

Members of the family Hylidae are, for lack of a better English word, also commonly called frogs. This family comprises the tree frogs (genus *Hyla*), cricket frogs (genus *Acris*), and chorus frogs (genus *Pseudacris*). In appearance and behavior, they differ greatly from the true frogs, or Ranidae. With the exception of some members of the tree frogs, most Hylidae are tiny creatures compared to the usually fairly large Ranidae. While no member of the Ranidae family is capable of climbing, tree frogs, as the name implies, are excellent climbers, aided by adhesive disks at the ends of their 'toes. Whereas all Ranidae have smooth and moist skins, the skins of many members of the family Hylidae are warty, rough, and dry. In addition, almost all hylid frogs have single, external vocal pouches, whereas the vocal pouches of most ranid frogs are paired.

While tree frogs are discussed in a separate entry (see *Tree Frog*), a few representative species of the family Ranidae, as well as of the genus *Acris* and of the genus *Pseudacris*, are described as follows.

The genus *Pseudacris* comprises several species of very small frogs commonly known as chorus frogs, or swamp cricket frogs, although the true cricket frogs belong to a different genus. They congregate in large numbers in or around shallow waters, where, during the breeding season, their whistling or rasping calls resemble the sound of a stick run along a picket fence and often ascending in scale. Whereas the tree frogs (genus *Hyla*) are excellent climbers, thanks to adhes-

Green frogs are common in eastern swamps and marshes

ive pads on their toes, and cricket frogs (genus *Acris*) do not climb at all, chorus frogs are capable of some climbing on weeds or low shrubs. Chorus frogs are widely distributed through the United States, although in certain regions, notably New England, they are absent. Due to their small size and great variation, they are not easy to identify, but small toe disks and a light line along the upper lip may serve as identification marks for many of them. Adult chorus frogs feed on tiny insects, spiders, and possibly other small arthropods (*See Arthropods*).

The frogs of the genus *Acris* probably derive their name—cricket frog—from their clicking call, which is often reminiscent of pebbles being clicked together. They are tiny frogs, rarely much more than one inch in length, with moist, warty skin. Generic identification is easily made by the fact that they have a dark triangle between their eyes and a dark stripe, or stripes, on their thighs. Identification of the various species is extremely difficult, however, because of the many color variations that may occur. Their distribution is similar to that of the chorus frogs, but on the eastern seaboard they range somewhat farther north. They are highly gregarious and can be found in large groups in or near shallow water.

Cricket frogs are excellent jumpers, and their zig-zagging leaps make their capture difficult. They are, however, entirely incapable of climbing. The adults feed on tiny insects and spiders. —G.P.

FROGS & TOADS

American toad

Fowler's toad

Bullfrog

Swamp cricket frog

Tree toad

Spadefoot toad

Green frog

Peeper

Meadow, or leopard, frog

Pickerel frog

Wood frog

Mink frog

Cricket frog

Bullfrog
Other Common Names—None
Scientific Name—*Rana catesbeiana*
Family—Ranidae (true frogs)
Order—Salienta
Size—Length, 3½ to 8 inches
Range—From Nova Scotia throughout most of the United States east of the Rocky Mountains, except southern Florida. Has been introduced into many locations west of the Rocky Mountains

The fully grown bullfrog is easily identified, as it is the largest frog in the United States. Its color ranges from green to brown, sometimes mottled or marked, sometimes plain. Although younger specimens may resemble green frogs, the latter have ridges on the sides of their backs that are absent in the bullfrog. The best identification is the call of the male, which is the well-known and unmistakable *jug-a-rum*. Bullfrogs are strictly aquatic and can be found sitting near the shoreline of ponds, frequently half submerged in duckweed.

Mating takes place from April to July, depending on the latitude. The female deposits thousands of eggs that, surrounded by their gelatinous envelopes, can be found floating like a lace net on the surface of the water in spring and summer. The tadpoles that emerge from the eggs may take as much as two years before transforming into adult frogs; prior to completion of the transformation a bullfrog tadpole may measure more than six inches. Bullfrogs are highly voracious and will try to devour anything that moves. They feed not only on insects but also on snakes, mice, bats, birds, and smaller frogs. The bullfrog population has been severely decimated in many places by man, who considers its legs a delicacy.   —G.P.

Green Frog
Other Common Names—None
Scientific Name—*Rana clamitans*
Family—Ranidae (true frogs)
Order—Salienta
Size—Length, 2¼ to 4 inches
Range—East from Canada to South Carolina, and west from Minnesota to Oklahoma

This is probably the most common true frog within its range. It can be found almost anywhere in or near bodies of fresh water. Somewhat resembling a small bullfrog, it can be easily distinguished by its smaller size, more slender appearance, and the presence of ridges or folds along its upper sides. Its color may range anywhere from green to brown. The belly is white, and the throat of the adult male is yellow. The male's call is a banjo-like *ploink* that can be heard on warm spring and summer evenings.

Breeding takes place anytime between April and August, depending on the latitude. The eggs, numbering in the thousands, are laid in a surface film. The emerging tadpole completes its transformation the following spring.   —G.P.

Leopard Frog
Other Common Names—Meadow frog
Scientific Name—*Rana pipiens*
Family—Ranidae (true frogs)
Order—Salienta
Size—Length, two to four inches
Range—Leopard frogs inhabit most of the United States and Canada, as far west as the Pacific States

This frog has long served as a valuable laboratory animal. In size and color it is similar to the green frog, but the leopard frog can be easily identified by the irregularly placed dark, rounded blotches with light borders, prominent on the back, sides, head, and legs. This marking differentiates it also from another member of the same genus, the pickerel frog, *Rana palustris*, whose blotches, without light borders, are square in two parallel rows.

Although the habitat of the leopard frog is usually close to fresh water, it can, on occasion, be found quite far away in moist meadows—thus its other common name of meadow frog.

Wood frog

The call of the male is a low, guttural snore; it can most frequently be heard during the breeding season, which comes rather early, usually in April. The tadpoles that emerge from the flattened spherelike egg mass require from two to three months to complete their transformation into adult frogs. —G.P.

Wood Frog
Other Common Names — Forest frog
Scientific Name — *Rana sylvatica*
Family — Ranidae (true frogs)
Order — Salienta
Size — Length, 1 ½ to 3¼ inches
Range — Across the North American continent from Labrador to Alaska. In the East, the range extends as far south as the southern Appalachians; in the West the southern part of the range extends south to the Canadian border. It has the northernmost range of all American amphibians.

The wood frog is a strikingly beautiful frog. Bronze or beige in color, it has a dark mask extending backward from the eyes, which makes the frog easy to identify. However, during the mating season the body color may turn drab brown or gray which blends with the decayed leaves submerged in the breeding ponds. As the name implies, the wood frog is a denizen of the woods, often wandering far from the water. Early in spring wood frogs congregate in large numbers in woodland pools that may still be partly covered by ice. Their mating call, resembling the quacking of ducks or the creaking of a wheel, can be heard throughout the woods. After breeding is completed, they leave the water and do not return to it again until the following spring. The eggs are laid in gelatinous clusters, which are attached to the submerged branches of trees. Each cluster may contain 2,000 to 3,000 eggs. Transformation of the tadpoles to adults takes from 1½ to 3 months. —G.P.

FROGHOPPER AND TREEHOPPER
Froghoppers

In countless fields throughout the land there can be seen during each summer thousands of little masses of bubbles attached to grasses, flowers, and shrubs. It is said that country people believe that frogs were responsible for spitting up these little bubbles in the grass; thus they were called *frog spit* or *frog foam*. Actually, these mounds of bubbles are the foam homes of peculiar pygmy insects, commonly called froghoppers because in shape they resemble tiny frogs and can leap about. More accurately, they are the homes of young, or pre-adult, froghoppers in the nymphal stage. These cercopids (family Cercopeidae of the order Homoptera), builders of the snowy bubble mounds, are relatives of the shrilling cicada, whose piercing song can be heard during the late summer (*See under Cicada*).

Bubble-building froghoppers are often less than an eighth of an inch in length. Usually, the nymphs, or young froghoppers, are of a pale, yellowish or greenish-yellow color. The mature insects, however, are most often of a dull brown or gray color. They are rather inconspicuous insects—small in size, drab in color.

The volume of sap this tiny insect can drain from a plant in a matter of minutes is impressive. It has been reported that a few dozen of a species found in Madagascar are able to produce, through combined effort, a full quart of liquid in the space of less than two hours. Sometimes two or more of these insect nymphs will work together under the cover of a single bubble nest.

One foreign species, which is larger in size than any American froghopper, is said to inhabit certain trees in great numbers, and, as a result of their sap-sucking activities, there is an almost constant dripping of fluid from the twig tips. The legend of the rain tree, or weeping tree, has its origin here.

The manner in which these cercopids build their bubble nests has been the subject of much debate. Some observers have claimed that they are produced by the insect whisking its tail about, like a miniature eggbeater, until the surplus liquid that is emitted from the tip of the abdomen is beaten into a bubbly froth. Other commentators skim lightly over the matter, saying "bubbles are blown from the tip of the abdomen." However the French naturalist, Jean Henri Fabre, "that incomparable observer" as Darwin called him, reported long ago that the insect is equipped not only for blowing bubbles, but also for gauging their size. Fabre then went on to explain where the air-measuring apparatus is located in the body of the young froghopper and how it operates.

Situated in the froghopper's hind end, at the tip of the abdomen, is a little pocket which opens to the atmosphere by means of a Y-shaped orifice. When the insect raises its tail tip, the lips of this orifice open, permitting a small volume of air to rush into the tiny pocket, where it is trapped as the lips of the opening close. Then, the tail descends into the pool of viscid liquid that has been eliminated from the insect's body after having been processed within its digestive tract. As the tip of the abdomen is submerged in the liquid, the trapped air is released, creating a small, glistening bubble. This, then, is the secret blowing apparatus, the miniature bellows that collects, measures, and delivers the air used in blowing the bubbles. When the up-tail-down-tail action is repeated many times, the froghopper is hidden from sight, covered by a protective envelope of bubbles.

Life for the froghopper, snug within its bubble home, is one round after another of almost constant sap-bibbing. As the vital fluid of the plant passes through the pygmy's digestive tract, cer-

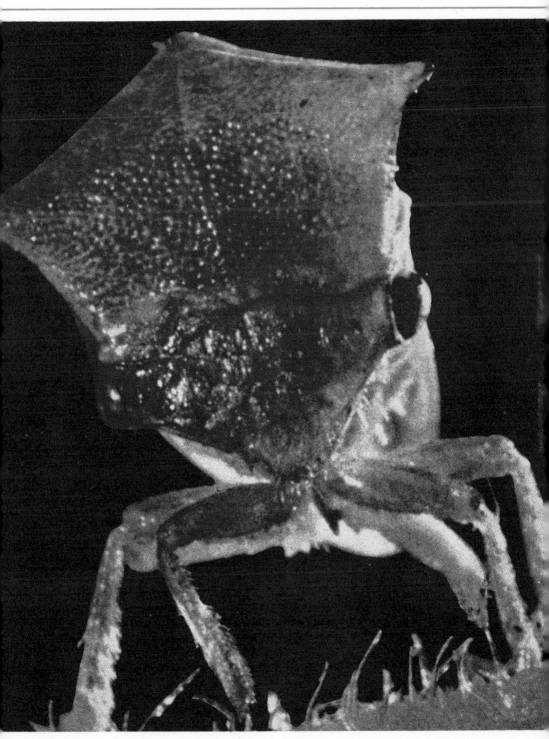

Buffalo treehoppers live in grassy fields until they are mature; then they migrate to trees and shrubs

tain nourishing food elements are removed, glandular secretions are picked up, and the surplus liquid is eliminated from its body. Once the insect has blown itself a complete home, it has no need of the relatively large volume of fluid that constantly wells from the tip of its abdomen as it feeds. This liquid collects in a pool around its body until the effect of surface tension can no longer compete with the pull of gravity, and the liquid runs down the plant stem.

Just why does the froghopper go through the strenuous routine of building a bubble house? The point is still being debated by scientists. However, it would appear that this frothy envelope has several important functions, which seem quite obvious after a little careful observation.

In the first place, the bubble nest protects the tiny froghopper—a rather delicately constituted insect—from the desiccating effects of a dry atmosphere. Secondly, these insects are sensitive to bright light and excessive heat. A third reason for the bubble nest is that it makes an effective barrier which protects the cercopid from attack by predatory insects. Even so, there is one tiny wasp that does prey on the froghoppers. "It drags the baby hoppers," writes Edwin Way Teale, "from these foaming retreats and carries them away to fill the larder for its unborn young."

At the beginning of the froghopper season, the bubble nests are small; but as the season progresses, larger ones are built. Increasing in size as it approaches adulthood, the insect must of necessity have larger and larger homes.

With the last molt, at which time its wings make an appearance, the diminutive insect emerges as an adult. Its once foamy, glistening house of bubbles, empty save for the discarded nymphal skin, is dried and broken, left to crumble away to dust.

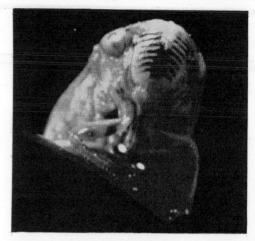

Adult froghopper resembles its close relative, the cicada

Froghopper nymphs on a stem above their bubble home

Treehoppers

Treehoppers, or membracids, are closely related to the bubble-blowing froghoppers. They are extremely grotesque pygmy insects. In fact, they are so strange that their forms "suggest that they are creatures of an unhealthy imagination rather than living facts." The quotation is taken from the writings of Edward Step, who goes even further and suggests that the tiny creatures should be called "nightmare insects."

These peculiar pygmies seem deformed and ludicrous in appearance. In most, the prothorax is broken up by lumps, bumps, and humps, and adorned with horns, bulbs, knobs, spines, notches, rods, and blisters. Indeed, some are so constructed that it is impossible to describe them. These forms are, for the most part, to be found in Central and South America, although many North American species are quite as grotesque.

Although they are commonly called treehoppers, quite as many species inhabit the grasses and weeds as those that live among the trees and shrubs. Furthermore, many that are found as adults in the trees spend their preadult, or nymphal state, among the succulent weeds. These insects, like their cercopid relatives, subsist upon plant juices.

One species of small treehopper found among the grasses and weeds is scarcely a fifth of an inch in length, exclusive of its forward-protruding "horn." This insect has no common name, being known only by its scientific designation, *Campylenchia latipes*, which, as printed here, is several times longer than the insect itself. Nymphs of this species not only have a horn that juts forward at a jaunty angle, but also a row of tiny notches down their backs.

While examining some nettle plants, a person may find a minute humpbacked insect. This is another species of treehopper that has been given no common name. It is usually found on no other

Treehopper nymph on a blade of grass

plant. Scientists call it *Entylia bactriana*.

In a census of the little humpbacked treehoppers living in a clump of nettle plants, one might count more than 80 of them in one small patch of weeds. While counting the insects, one may notice that many of the nettle leaves have brownish streaks along the underside of the midvein that cause the leaves to bend back as though broken. On examining these brownish streaks closely through a powerful magnifying glass, one can discern a series of minute specks embedded in the veins of the fractured leaves. The streaks are tiny scores made by the treehopper's ovipositor, or egg-laying apparatus, as she deposits her tiny seeds of life (the specks) within the tissues of the midvein.

Most, if not all, treehoppers lay their eggs in the midvein of leaves or in grass stems. Female buffalo treehoppers, for example, lay their eggs in parallel, crescent-shaped punctures in the twigs and branches of such trees as elm, hawthorn, and apple, often causing considerable damage by weakening these members. The eggs hatch during the following spring and the nymphs start to feed on the juices of clover or of other plants. After the young buffalo treehoppers have molted several times, they gain their wings and become full-fledged adult insects. As adults they continue to feed on juicy weeds and grasses, but as fall approaches they migrate to trees and shrubs, where they breed and lay the eggs that will carry the species through the winter. In spring the cycle is repeated. —H.V.G.

Hoarfrost at Niagara Falls, New York

FROST

Because they are so familiar, things near at hand are often neglected by people in a search far afield for rarities. Not only the winter sportsman and the naturalist, but the dweller in crowded cities can enjoy and appreciate the wonderful, white, sparkling world of snow and ice, to which the "open sesame" is the freezing temperature 32° Fahrenheit. At this temperature water becomes a crystalline solid known in its various forms as snow, frost, rime, sleet, glaze, or ice. The particles of water that at temperatures above freezing slide freely over one another in a liquid, at freezing temperature become arranged into crystals of hexagonal, or six-sided, symmetry. One can see these crystals best in snow.

Snow

The delicate details and endless variety of snowflakes result from their formation directly from water vapor in the clouds at temperatures sometimes far below freezing. All are six-sided, the more solid crystals being formed in the intense cold of the higher clouds; the exquisite feathery forms develop in lower clouds where the air is still, the moisture plentiful, and the temperature only a little below freezing.

If the temperatures are very low the crystals may be needlelike. The temperature of the air drops on an average of 1° Fahrenheit for every 300-foot rise in altitude. The cirrus clouds that float high above the surface of the earth are composed of these fine ice crystals (*See under Cloud*).

The best time to observe snow crystals is soon after a storm begins. Later the crystals collide and stick together as they fall, making large shapeless flakes. Snow is white because many, many, tiny reflecting surfaces are formed on the crystal particles and air spaces are trapped between these.

More snow falls on mountains than in lowlands. On the western slopes of the Sierra Nevada and Cascade ranges over 400 inches of snow a year is not uncommon. During one year almost 790 inches of snow fell on Mount Rainier at an elevation of 5,500 feet. In the eastern United States, annual snowfalls of 50 to 100 inches occur as far south as West Virginia along the Appalachian Mountains. In the region of the Great Lakes there is also a fairly heavy snowfall, which in some places may reach more than 100 inches annually.

Hoarfrost

Sometimes, after a cold, clear, still night, one may wake up to find the world blanketed with glittering white hoarfrost. On such a night the heat from the ground radiates out into space. The air immediately above the ground becomes cold and, if the temperature drops below freezing, the moisture in the air crystallizes on trees, shrubs, and ground as hoarfrost. On windy nights the moisture-laden cold air near the ground is mixed with the warmer air above, preventing the formation of hoarfrost. If the temperature were higher, this moisture would condense as dew. The film of moisture that forms on the outside of a pitcher of cold water on a warm day is a common phenomenon. This film has condensed from the water vapor in the air, much the same way as dew or frost.

Often the hoarfrost appears as small globules. This happens when the air is warm in the early part of the evening and the moisture is deposited as dew. Later the temperature goes below freezing and the droplets of dew become globules of ice. Fine, feathery frost crystals are formed only when the temperature is below freezing during the entire night. Cloudy nights are usually frostless because the clouds prevent radiation of the ground heat. When the citrus groves of Florida and California are threatened by frost the owners make clouds of smoke in smudge pots. These smoke clouds prevent the loss of heat from the orchard and thus protect the delicate citrus fruit from frost.

Rime

Sometimes, on mountain tops, all objects become covered on the windward side with masses of crystals resembling hoarfrost. Unlike hoarfrost, however, these frost crystals are deposited on windy days. As a frosty fog drifts along on the wind of a freezing day, masses of loose, feathery ice crystals, called rime, are deposited on whatever the fog drifts against. Occasionally, rime is several inches thick and the crystals may be an inch long, sparkling with great beauty in the sunlight.

Sleet and Hail

Sleet is usually composed of frozen raindrops, but may be formed under more complex conditions. From clouds high in the air snow falls. During its descent to earth this snow meets warmer air and becomes partly melted. Finally, near the ground it enters a layer of cold air in which it is again frozen. Usually, sleet is associated with snow and ice storms.

Although sleet is sometimes called hail, true hail occurs only in the summertime during violent thunderstorms. Hailstones start as small pellets of ice or snow that fall part way to the earth and then are carried back into the cold, upper cloud regions by the strong upward blasts of air in a thundercloud. At the top of the cloud they fall out of these blasts, only to be returned in other upward air currents. Sometimes hailstones repeat this circuit several times, the pellets growing larger with each journey. Each time the pellets partly melt as they fall and refreeze as they rise. In the upper regions of the cloud more snow is accumulated over the layer of ice that had just formed on the way up. An open hail pellet will disclose the concentric layers of ice and snow.

Glaze

Perhaps the most spectacular form of ice is the brilliant, sparkling coating of houses, trees, wires, fences, and the ground with a smooth, icy glaze. Although often called a sleetstorm, this glaze is formed under different condi-

Glaze on rhododendron

tions. After a long cold spell or a crisp, cold night in winter has reduced everything to below freezing, rain may fall from warm air masses above the cold air near the ground. As soon as this rain hits the cold objects near the ground, it freezes into the smooth coating of ice that is called glaze. When heavy masses of this ice accumulate on trees and wires they bend and break, doing much damage to property. Roads may become dangerously icy or impassable in such icestorms.

Ice

The formation of ice on the surfaces of ponds and lakes protects the animal life beneath. Ponds lose their heat from the surface, and as they cool the cold water sinks, until the entire pond is at a temperature of about 39° F. When the water on the top of the pond becomes still colder, instead of sinking, it becomes lighter, and remains on top. This top water freezes when it cools to 32° F. Ice weighs about a tenth less than an equal volume of water and thus floats with about a tenth of its bulk above water. Immediately below the ice the water is a little warmer than freezing; but toward the bottom of the pond the temperature remains at about 39° F. all winter long. In this warmer water fishes, amphibians, turtles, and other forms of life in the pond can remain active even during the most severe winters (*See under Pond*).   —J.W.T., Jr.

Snow crystals

FUNGUS

Fungi (funguses) may be found almost anywhere. They are on objects we touch, on our clothing and skin, and in the air we breathe. They may be found in the soil in their growing, vegetative stage or as microscopic reproductive bodies called spores. Some fungi live in water and others live as parasites in the tissues of plants and animals. Most of these are harmless to man even though they may be present as spores in all of these places.

Fungi are usually tiny plants without root, stem, or leaf and are represented by such forms as mushrooms, toadstools, mildews, rusts, smuts, and molds. They are classed as plants because of their structure and method of reproduction, but the ways in which they secure food are strikingly different from the process of photosynthesis used by ordinary green plants. Green plants can take water and minerals from the soil and carbon dioxide from the air and make carbohydrates from them. The carbohydrates can then be used for growth. Fungi cannot manufacture carbohydrates because they do not possess green chlorophyll. They get their food for growth by one of two methods: They use dead plants or animals, or they use living plants or animals. Fungi in the first group are called *saprophytes;* those in the second group are called *parasites.*

Some fungi secure their foods simply by absorbing the sugars, water, and minerals from the material upon which they grow. For example, the molds sometimes found on jelly or jam can get at least some food directly in this manner. Far more frequently, the process is not so simple. Usually a spore of a fungus will alight upon a food the fungus cannot absorb directly. It must first break the food down into simpler chemicals that are soluble and can be absorbed. This is done through the action of enzymes secreted by the fungus. The enzymes change a complex food into simpler foods. For example, starch is changed into a glucose sugar that can be absorbed by the fungus.

Many raw materials can be used as

Fungi growing on a birch

foods by various fungi. Molds growing on damp shoe leather are able to secrete enzymes that make certain substances in the leather suitable as food. The dark spots sometimes appearing on damp cotton clothing left wet or in contact with the ground are patches of mold that can change the cellulose of the cloth to food. The bluish-green molds visible in certain kinds of cheese are able to grow there because they can use food materials in the cheese. During their growth molds also produce chemicals that give some of the distinctive odors and flavors to different cheeses.

The term mold is used to describe fungus growths that are more or less fluffy or woolly in appearance and that are found on bread or other foods or in damp soil or wood. They actually represent only a few members of the large group of plants called fungi.

In the soil, whether it is covered by a lawn, garden, or woodland, the fungi are quite numerous. This is due to the great abundance of such food materials as leaves, twigs, and the dead roots and stems of plants. Different fungi use different substances in feeding on these materials so that the dead plants are finally completely disintegrated.

In damp summer or fall weather various fungi, especially mushrooms, toadstools, and puffballs of various sorts, may become quite plentiful in lawns. If the lawn is on a former woodland area, the fungi will be chiefly those of the woods because their growing vegetative stage is still present in the soil. Each year this underground threadlike portion, the *mycelium,* which consists of masses of elongated cells that fork and branch and under favorable conditions grow very rapidly, will continue to decay suitable materials in the soil. When conditions are right, the mycelium produces the spore-bearing portion such as the mushroom or bracket fungus. Eventually, when the food supply is used up, all will probably disappear. Fungi of meadow and field may be introduced in the topsoil and persist for a number of years.

Fungi in Dead Tissues

The destruction of organic matter is not brought about by one kind of fungus but by a number of different kinds that operate at the same time or that succeed one another. The decay of a log, tree, or stump may be started by one of a number of fungi brought to the wood by air currents carrying the spores. On the other hand, destruction may already be in progress due to some wood-rotting fungus that has attacked the tree while it was standing. After some time, these fungi may find conditions unfavorable to them or may no longer be able to keep out other species, and so a new group of fungi attack the partially decayed wood. These new plants may be followed in a year or so by another group. Eventually all that remains of the tree or stump is an outline of brown, dry, friable tissue that is not yet destroyed. Even this may later be slowly changed by the growth of mosses or small seed-plants that will help convert it into woodland humus (*See also under Tree*).

Disintegration occurs slowly and inexorably, but changes can be seen in only a few years' time, such as the decay of leaves in a forest. In the summer or fall the leaves just below the surface of the forest floor are held together by mats of white or brightly colored vegetative mycelium of various fungi, especially mushrooms. These leaves already show some signs of decay —the mycelium has been using cellulose or sugars in the leaves as a source of food. A year later, at the same spot, the leaves, now farther below the surface, will be more decayed. In another year or so, all resemblance to leaves will be gone. All these changes can be seen at one time by digging deeper into the leaf mold.

The decay of dead plants and animals is of value in two ways. If it were not for this destructive action, dead materials would eventually accumulate to such an extent that the earth would be covered by them. More important is the fact that when dead materials undergo disintegration, the carbon in them is changed to carbon dioxide again. It can then be used by green plants in the manufacture of foods that they, other animals, and human beings, can use.

Fungi in Living Tissue

Most plant diseases are caused by different species of fungi that grow into or through the tissue of the plant. Absorption of foods from the plant will allow the fungus to continue to grow but will also weaken the plant so that it cannot make sufficient food to keep alive. (It seems likely that some fungi secrete a toxin that kills the plant.) Shade trees infected by wood-rotting fungi become so weakened that they blow over easily, and forest trees lose value as timber because the wood may be almost completely destroyed by the fungus. Leaf spots, rust diseases, smuts, mildew, and blights are all caused by fungi.

A few fungi are parasitic upon animals. Ringworm and athlete's foot are caused by fungi growing in the skin, and a few rare fungi cause more serious diseases. Birds, fishes, and flies sometimes are infected by fungi.

Fungi and Man

Fungi are extremely important in the destruction of many materials. Sometimes their activities are spectacular. The sudden appearance of crops of mushrooms and the devastating attacks of fungous diseases are striking. More often their activities are slow, quiet, and insidious. Any food materials in storage are likely to spoil; corn and wheat may be molded so badly that a great loss results; dairy products may be spoiled by the growth of bacteria and molds; eggs and meat may become moldy. Telephone and electrical power companies are always faced with the problem of rotting timbers as well as destruction of insulating material around underground cables. Ropes, twines, and sacking materials constantly exposed to the elements eventually may be weakened or destroyed by the activity of fungi.

Many fungi are of interest for another reason: They produce certain important chemicals. Yeast, during its growth, produces carbon dioxide that causes dough to rise before it is baked. Yeast also can be grown to produce alcohol. Certain molds give flavor to cheese, as mentioned earlier. Some mushrooms and truffles are edible. A number of acids that are used in medicine, cooking, or manufacturing processes are produced by molds, and several vitamins are made from others. Probably the most exciting products are the antibiotics. These are chemicals that prevent the growth of

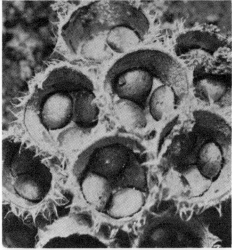

Top: *Inky cap mushrooms, the spore-bearing part of a common fungus.* Middle: *Bird-nest fungus. Each "egg" in these fungus "nests" contains thousands of spores.* Bottom: *When mature, these spore-bearing puffballs spurt clouds of spores through the opening on top. The impact of raindrops will cause these balls to emit spores, like smoke*

or actually kill microorganisms. Those antibiotics that are harmless to persons may be used for treatment of certain diseases. Most of those in use at the present time are produced by molds; penicillin, the first one found to be useful, is produced commercially by a strain of *Penicillium chrysogenum*. Streptomycin, aureomycin, and terramycin are produced by other moldlike organisms originally found in the soil.

Appearance and Reproduction

The spores referred to earlier are of various shapes, colors, and sizes, but all are too small to be seen without a microscope. Some fungi produce few spores, but most kinds produce many and some produce tremendous numbers. For example, it has been calculated that a fairly large specimen of *Agaricus arvensis*, a mushroom, produces 16 billion spores. A large specimen of *Fomes applanatus*, one of the bracket, or shelf, fungi on trees, produces 30 million spores each day, and this fungus continues to produce at this rate for several months; in fact, about 5,500,000,000,000 spores would be produced in one season. As happens with reproductive cells or offspring of other forms of life only a few of all of these spores manage to survive.

The spore is carried by some means (most often, wind) away from the parent. If there is moisture, if the temperature is favorable, and if there is suitable food material, the spore will begin to grow. At first a tubular, or pipelike, branching thread is formed. Each of these threads is called a *hypha*. A mass of hyphae constitute the vegetative part of the fungus, the mycelium.

These hyphae secrete the enzymes, then absorb the food produced, which may be used for further growth or stored for future use. They grow farther and farther into the log, or plants, or other suitable material, using it as food and changing it into a decaying mass.

At some time the fungus will reproduce itself. This is accomplished in many different ways. Some small fungi produce a few spores in a simple manner. Some, like bread mold, produce spores inside a small swelling that dries out and breaks open to release the spores to the wind. Other fungi grow for some time and then produce a complex structure such as a mushroom, cup fungus, or bracket fungus that forms the spores.

A fungus does not necessarily produce spores and die. This may occur, but more often a fungus will persist in a vegetative condition long after the spores are liberated. Whenever conditions are right it will again produce more spores. Mushrooms, for example, may be found in the same area year after year where their vegetative plant body continues to live.

Spore Distribution

Spores of fungi growing in water are carried by water currents. Spores of fungi growing in the soil may be spread by water movement following rains. In fact, raindrops themselves aid in dispersal of some spores. The impact of raindrops falling on puffballs causes spores to be blown out into the air, and heavy raindrops will splash the "eggs" out of birds'-nest fungi. The "eggs," incidentally, are very small thick disks that contain thousands of spores.

Flies disseminate the spores of the evil-smelling stinkhorns. The odor of the

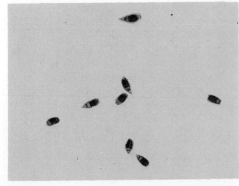

Many kinds of spores are produced by the different fungi

tissue producing the spores is attractive to carrion flies which walk among the spores and then carry them away on their feet. Birds, too, probably often step into the masses of spores produced by many of the fungi growing on the bark of trees and thus help to spread the spores. Beetles are known to transmit spores of fungi on their bodies, and some of our serious tree diseases are spread by them (*See under Chestnut and under Elm*).

Wind, however, probably distributes the spores of most fungi. Once a spore is discharged from its place of formation a very slight current of air will carry it some distance. Collections of air samples reveal spores may be carried thousands of feet high and even into northern Canada near the Arctic. Most of these die en route, but obviously the wind can bring about a wide distribution of fungi. If they find suitable conditions for growth, the plants become widespread.

Another example that illustrates the role of the wind in disseminating spores, as well as the vast amount of spore material produced and the serious results of the activity of fungi, has been discovered recently. It has been known for some time that certain spores of stem rust of wheat can be carried to new, disease-free wheat plants by the wind. During a four-day period of windy weather, wheat-rust spores that were produced on wheat growing in central Oklahoma and south central Kansas, thrown into the air during harvesting, were blown to fields of wheat in eastern North Dakota and South Dakota, northwestern Iowa, and western Minnesota, an area of more than 40,000 square miles. It was estimated that 4,000 tons of spores were produced in the Oklahoma-Kansas area. Six hundred pounds of these spores were carried to the northern area mentioned above, fell on the wheat stems and infected them. The growing rust fungus robbed the wheat plant of food it had made and thus lowered the yield of grain harvested.

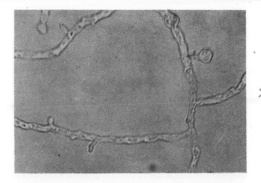

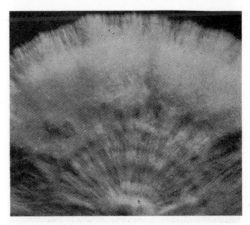

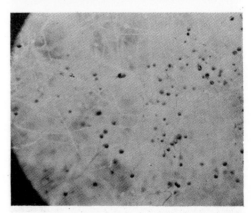

Top: *When the spore of a fungus starts to grow, it produces branching threadlike hyphae (magnified about 400 times).*
Middle: *A mass of hyphae is known as mycelium. These are radiating from the spot where growth began (natural size).*
Bottom: *The black spots are small sacs containing the microscopic spores of bread molds (these are magnified about three times)*

That spores of different fungi are in the air can be demonstrated easily by exposing Petri dishes filled with some suitable nutrient such as gelatin to the air for a few days. In lieu of a Petri dish a slice of bread that has been moistened with a few drops of water can be used. Expose the slice for 10 or 15 minutes and then store in a warm place under some cover so it will not dry out. One will be rewarded, or dismayed, by the different kinds of molds that develop.
—J.B.R.

Recommended Reading

Introductory Mycology—Constantine John Alexopoulos. John Wiley & Sons. New York.

The Molds and Man—Clyde M. Christensen. University of Minnesota Press. Minneapolis.

The Mushroom Hunter's Field Guide—Alexander H. Smith. University of Michigan Press, Ann Arbor, Michigan.

Fungi—Gertrude McWilleams. National Audubon Society Nature Program Guide No. 60. Doubleday & Company. Garden City, New York.

Mushroom and Other Fungi: Their Form and Color—H. Kleign. Doubleday & Company. Garden City, New York.

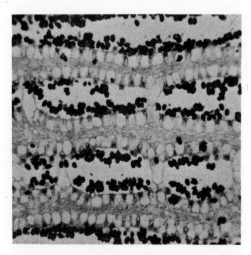

Highly magnified undersurface of an inky cap mushroom. The dark spots are the spores. These develop from special cells on the surface of the radiating leaflike plates, or gills, that make up the underside of these mushrooms

Fungi—Friends of the Forest

Foresters may raise their eyebrows and brand as heretical the suggestion that fungi are their friends. Colleges of forestry teach identification and control of tree-destroying species, and it is a matter of record that almost 10 percent of our American forest crop is killed, damaged, or degraded by fungous attacks. Few foresters, however, give serious thought to the fact that there would not be any forests if it were not for omnipresent fungi that reduce dead timber and forest litter to essential humus on the woodland floor.

Without the sanitary services of fungi, the original forests that immigrants found on the North American continent would have accumulated forest debris from decade to decade until the huge unaltered woodpile was ignited by lightning or by an aboriginal campfire. The resulting conflagration would have reduced the forest and its topsoil to a sterile desert.

While certain fungi are justly accused of killing trees, those attacks are mostly on overmature stands, which now are diminishing in volume and importance as advances to younger managed forests are made. And under future forest management tree-killing fungi should be reasonably controlled.

Even under the most competent management, however, forests will need fungi, which with the help of bacteria and insects will continue to convert stumps, tops, leaves, fallen limbs, and cones into the blanket of humus, which protects tree roots, retards water runoff, and later integrates with mineral soil.

For every destructive species, there are at least a score of saprophytic fungi that constantly produce mulch from useless wood. Some species act in a dual capacity, as does *Armillaria mellea*, a destructive tree-killer but also a disintegrator of stumps and of dead and useless timber. Its cousin, *A. ponderosa*, is a saprophyte that lives on decaying wood, and incidentally produces a choice edible mushroom that grows commonly

Fungi growing on decaying wood

in the coniferous forests of the Pacific Northwest. So abundant is this esculent product of forest waste that local Japanese collect and sell it by the ton.

The coral fungus, *Hydnum coralloides*, also doubles as a forest sanitarian and food supplier. Its saprophytic activities, especially in dense Engelmann spruce forests, accelerate the decay of stumps and dead roots, of which the end product emerges in the form of large tufts of interlacing edible branches. Competition for this forest delicacy is so keen that, unless it is collected within a few hours after its emergence, insects and rodents will have beaten the human mushroom hunter to the draw.

The fruiting bodies of nearly every forest saprophyte, in fact, furnish food for some forest habitant—bear, deer, rodent, bird, or insect. One exception is *Daedalea unicolor*, a rapid and efficient destroyer of hardwood forest debris, whose sporophores are too tough to be eaten by man or beast.

Two other saprophytes—*Amanita muscaria* and *A. pantherina* (*See under Amanita*)—are instinctively avoided by forest birds and other animals because of their extreme toxicity, although they are occasionally eaten with fatal results by humans. However, eastern red squirrels often eat the deadly amanitas without being harmed by them. Perhaps other mammals, besides red squirrels, may eat mushrooms that are poisonous to humans, without suffering any harmful effects. *A. muscaria* has been used in insecticidal solutions. Its pantherine cousin is even more lethal than *A. muscaria* when taken internally.

To atone for these two killers, northwestern forests supply the animal kingdom with two delicious edible fungi—*Coprinus comatus*, shaggy mane, and *Morchella esculenta*, the popular morel. These grow in profusion on sheep bedding sites and corrals, which are numerous on most high altitude forest stock ranges. Bushels of morels and shaggy

POISONOUS OR UNPALATABLE SPECIES

Fly mushroom (poison)

Destroying angel (poison)

False morel (suspected)

Oyster shell stereum

Scarlet cup

Jack-o'-lantern (poison)

Northern hydnum

Violet cortinarius

Frost's bolete (poison)

Rainbow conk

Varnished conk

EDIBLE SPECIES

Jeweled puffball

Chantrel

Coral fungus

Morel

Beefsteak mushroom

Chicken mushroom

Bear's head

Edible bolete

Mary Peck's russula

Shaggy mane

Delicious lactarius

Common field mushroom

manes may be collected on a single bedding ground after an early autumn rain.

The fruiting bodies of two species of *Mycena—epipterygia* and *galericulata—* are unbelievably fragile, but each species is a potent destroyer of waste forest wood. The latter works on decaying wood only, while the former specializes on dead branches and masses of fallen leaves. Another fragile wood destroyer, which forms huge clusters of fruiting bodies on old stumps, is *Coprinus micaceus.* Few forests in the United States are without its sanitary services.

One of the most minute and fragile forest saprophytes of the Pacific Northwest — *Collybia albipilata* — is ultradiscriminatory in its selection of a host. It not only specializes on coniferous cones, but confines itself to those of Douglas-fir (*See Douglas-fir*).

A fairly reliable forest hygrometer, as its name implies, is furnished by the saprophytic *Geastrum saccatum.* This *earth star,* growing in the forest debris of open woodlands, splits its outer peridium into numerous segments that spread downward in moist weather but retract upward around the spore-bearing inner peridium when humidity becomes low.

Fairy rings, ephemeral invaders of grassy plots, meadows, and forest glades, are produced by another saprophyte—*Marasmius oreades.* Its mycelia spread in an almost perfect circle from an underground accumulation of decaying plants, forming ever-widening circles with each generation of sporophores. Its economic value is probably far less than the enjoyment this mushroom gives to children in proving to them that fairies really exist (*See Children and Nature*).

Bacteria and insects materially assist saprophytic fungi in decomposing forest litter. Wood-boring beetles carry fungus spores into dead tree trunks and stumps. On the debit side of the forest ledger, however, they often carry such spores into living trees, as in the case of dendroctonus beetles boring into pine and pseudohylesinus beetles burrowing into white firs.

When those bark beetles approach population sizes disastrous to the forests, woodpeckers of many species mobilize to control the insects by chiseling through the thick outer bark for the succulent larvae. The lively tattoo of woodpecker battalions in beetle-infested pine forests is music to the ears of foresters (*See Biological Control*).

Other insects that collaborate with wood-destroying fungi are species of scarab beetles. They bury balls of manure that contain deposited eggs, and that often also contain fungus spores. The

Armillaria ponderosa *destroys forest litter under stands of pine*

A Douglas-fir cone is broken down by the tiny saprophyte, Collybia albipilata

spores germinate rapidly under such ideal conditions.

A working example of forest sanitation by fungi may be seen in Pacific Northwest forests that were logged in the wasteful days of high-stumping. When virgin timber was plentiful and cheap a generation ago, loggers usually felled the trees from "spring-boards" notched into tree trunks at distances of from 6 to 20 feet above the ground. Not only was it easier to cut trees well above the flaring bases, but also it was less work to saw and chop from springboards than from the brush-infested ground.

These enormous stumps still occupy a large portion of the forest floor in old cuttings, preventing reproduction of trees by natural seeding or by planting. Their removal would be expensive and stumps of western red cedar and Douglas-fir would remain almost intact if it were not for the destructive attacks of fungi and their natural allies.

During the long process of disintegration by fungi, each big stump becomes a fascinating community of plant and animal activity. Piles of crumbling wood accumulate around the base, furnishing a home for earthworms and insects. Cavities excavated by woodpeckers in search of grubs become repositories of native hazelnuts gathered by chipmunks and squirrels. When overlooked nuts germinate, the stump becomes festooned with hazel seedlings.

Birds that recently dined on mountain ash fruits and huckleberries roost on the stump with the eventual result that those two plants usually take over the upper strata. Windborne seeds from cedars and hemlocks lodge in the thick mass of fungi and moss that blankets the stump, so that it is not unusual to see trees 20 or 30 feet high growing atop the old forest veteran, their roots creeping down its sides to find lodgment in mineral soil. As the stump crumbles, these tree roots thicken to form a high arched crown above the pile of decaying wood.

Community life on and around the old stump is so complicated and interesting that it is easy for a person to lose sight of the basic business that is being transacted, namely the conversion of hundreds of cubic feet of waste wood into forest mulch. The livelihood of all inhabitants of the stump community depends upon the saprophytic fungi that are responsible for the initial breakdown of wood structure.

Perhaps the most interesting example of forest rehabilitation is in the unique rain forest of Olympic National Park.

Amanita muscaria *is a commonly found toxic fungus*

The delicate fungus, Mycena epipterygia, *rises on slender stalks*

Here for centuries forest giants have germinated, grown to maturity, died, and plunged to earth, to be dissected and returned to their elements by nature's expert technicians.

One hundred forty-two inches of annual precipitation keep the laboratory humidity at an optimum for fungous growth. Assisting the fungi are regiments of mosses, lichens, and ferns. Out of sight, in secret working cubicles, are armies of busy bacteria and insects, working to build the thick carpet of mulch that protects the life of the only great rain forest within the continental United States.   —D.H.C.

G

GALL
The Curious World of Plant Galls

When autumn leaves fall they reveal many of last summer's best-kept secrets. Keen-eyed naturalists find catbirds' nests tucked neatly away in fox grape tangles. They learn where woodchucks dug well-hidden burrows in briar patches. And they also discover the curious world of plant galls.

Galls are swellings or other deformities on stems, twigs, leaves, or roots. They are produced by a wide variety of organisms — insects, mites, fungi, and nematodes. An adult of the gall-making creature or organism attacks a particular region of a particular species of plant. Whether a plant spore or an insect's egg develops within the gall, the resulting gall closely resembles every other gall produced by that gall-making organism. Indeed, some naturalists find that certain plants—goldenrods, for example—are most accurately identified by first identifying their galls.

As the gall-maker develops, it irritates the plant tissues, either by its rasping action or by its secretions. The tissues then swell and oddly, the gall frequently encloses the organism that causes it, so the gall-maker is both protected and surrounded by its food supply.

Fully developed galls are sometimes more beautiful than any structure the plant normally produces. Flower galls on cypress, leaf spots on red maple, and hedgehog galls on white oak are striking objects.

Anyone who has ever puzzled over what appear to be crabapples under an oak tree has witnessed one example of a host's reaction to galls—the tree sheds them like ripe fruit. Farmers in Arkansas gather oak galls, which they call "oak wheat," from the ground for their stock and poultry food. Gamebirds also eat the galls.

Although most galls are biological curiosities without economic importance, some are serious pests. A mite causes pear leaves to blister, and a midge curls the leaves of apple trees. The notorious Hessian fly makes galls on wheat. In some areas of the United States, a midge prevents the production of clover seed. Aphids cause galls that mar the beauty of Norway and Colorado spruces. Other gall insects deform roses, violets, and chrysanthemums.

Some galls have surprising commercial uses. Certain oak galls, because of their very high tannic acid content, are peculiarly suited for making permanent inks and for dying wools and skins. Some produce incredible amounts of honeydew that bees gather and convert to honey.

Many things limit the production of galls. Weather is an important factor. A cold, rainy spring nearly wiped out the hedgehog galls on a white oak that was studied, yet the same weather seemed to favor two kinds of galls on witch hazel. Gall insects are weak fliers, hence stormy weather plays havoc with them. Of course, each gall-maker must begin life on the correct species of plant that is in just the right physiological condition.

Once started, the galls and their makers are harassed by parasites, mostly midges and wasps. Inquilines (flies) penetrate the developing galls and rob nourishment from the gall-makers. Woodpeckers, mice, and squirrels may attack a gall at any time for the tidbit within. (*See also Insect: Insect Gall-makers*).
　　　　　　　　　　　　—R.B.F.

Oak leaf galls are valuable for making inks and dyes

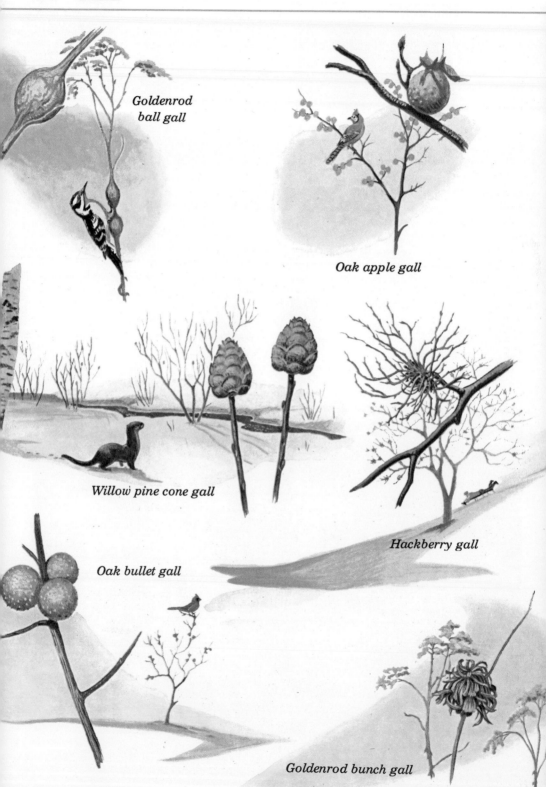

Goldenrod
ball gall

Oak apple gall

Willow pine cone gall

Hackberry gall

Oak bullet gall

Goldenrod bunch gall

Mossy rose gall

Sumac flower gall

Ash flower gall

Raspberry knot gall

Poplar vagabond gall

Locust twig gall

Goldenrod scarred gall

Pine cone gall

GALLINULE
Purple Gallinule
Other Common Names—Mudhen, swamp chicken
Scientific Name—*Porphyrula martinica*
Family—Rallidae (rails, gallinules, and coots)
Order—Gruiformes
Size—Length, 12 to 14 inches
Range—Breeds from the Carolinas south, occasionally wanders to New England

Long toes, suitable for walking on partly submerged water plants, are one of the distinguishing features of this colorful bird. The short, heavy beak is used to feed upon frogs, insects, grains, and flowers. A structure known as a frontal shield, with no known function, covers the forehead. The garish colors of the bird help to camouflage it in its watery home of green leaves, blue water, and bright flowers.

Gallinules are members of the order that includes the rails and the coots. All of these birds are long-legged, long-necked, and with bodies that are laterally compressed. These attributes assist them in slipping through heavy growths of reeds with little noise and surprising speed. The wings are short and rounded; the birds fly poorly, preferring to run to escape danger. Despite this, they are migratory, some of them crossing the Gulf of Mexico to winter in South America.

The nests are often built on islands of floating vegetation. The young are fully clothed in a black down at birth, and can run after the mother within a few hours after leaving the egg.

The common gallinule, *Gallinula chloropus*, of which the North American subspecies was formerly called the Florida gallinule, is a very similar bird to the moorhen of Europe and Asia. It resembles its purple relative very closely. Its plumage is drab by comparison, dull brown above and gray beneath, with a broken white line separating the two colors. —G.B.S.

The large toes of the purple gallinule make walking on partly submerged water plants and the large leaves of water lilies easy

An adult gannet is nearly the size of a large goose

GANNET
Other Common Names—Solan, solan goose
Scientific name—*Morus bassanus*
Family—Sulidae (boobies and gannets)
Order—Pelecaniformes
Size—Length, 35 to 40 inches
Range—Breeds on islands, in Gulf of St. Lawrence, Iceland, British Isles; winters southward to Florida and North Africa

The gannet is a large seabird, nearly the size of a large goose, and about twice the size of a herring gull. It has a heavy, straight bill, a stocky body, and a sharply pointed tail; when flying, it appears to be almost double-ended. Young birds are mottled, brown on white, but the adult is pure white with black outer wings, a yellow bill, and varying amounts of yellow on the head.

Fishes, especially herring and menhaden, are the food of the gannet.

Flocks of birds wheel and hover in the air over a school of fishes, each bird picking out a prospective victim and then launching itself on a steep dive from as much as one hundred feet. The impact of the bird's body sends spray ten feet high, and probably stuns a fish that is close to the surface. Air sacs, beneath the skin, cushion the blow to the internal organs of the bird. When fishes are schooling deeply, the gannet dives and then swims beneath the surface, using both wings and feet; they have been caught in nets at depths of 90 feet.

Gannets are awkward and uncomfortable on land and visit it only in the breeding season. The rest of the year they are out over the shallow waters of the coastal shelf, within several hundred miles of land, sleeping at night on the water. But when spring comes, each bird seeks out one of the 22 gannetries, or nesting sites, in the world. These must be rocky, isolated islands, free from predators. Only six of these gannetries are in North America.

The nesting territory of a pair of gannets is only a few square feet on level ground or on a rocky ledge that may look out over a sheer drop of hundreds of feet. The birds often cover the island with a living blanket of white. As many as 100,000 pairs have been recorded at one gannetry.

Both the male and the female build the nest, incubate the single egg, and care for the young. When the nestling is about twelve weeks old, the parents desert it. Usually it spends a week or so at the nest site, living on its own body fat, before it glides or falls from the cliff into the water, where it soon learns to fish for itself.

Gannets have few natural enemies. Killer whales have been caught with the gannet remains in their stomachs, and strayed chicks and untended eggs may be taken by skuas, jaegers, and gulls. Fishermen reduced the gannet population to the danger point in the past century, using the bodies of these tame, fearless birds as bait in fishtraps until the governments of the respective areas gave protection to the species.

One of the largest, and probably the most accessible of the gannetries on the Canadian coast is at Bonaventure Island, a mile or so from the Gaspe Peninsula. At least 7,000 birds breed there annually; accommodations for visitors and guide service are available.

Two other species of gannets occur in the southern hemisphere, one in Australia and the other in South Africa. Both of these are, like the northern gannet, cold-water birds. There are six species of tropical gannets, better known as boobies, occurring in nearly all the warm, shallow waters of the globe. Two of these (blue-faced booby, brown booby) occasionally appear at the Dry Tortu-

Gannets nest in colonies along sea cliffs

gas—small, sandy islands off the south-western tip of Florida. One other (blue-footed booby) has been recorded in south-eastern California and southwestern Arizona. The name *booby* was given to them because they are unafraid and trusting, and therefore very easy to kill.
—G.B.S.

GAR

A number of marine and freshwater species of fishes are known as gars. The name is likely to be attached to any fish with a long, slender body and an exceptionally long and narrow snout. Marine fishes of this type include the silver gar, or Atlantic needlefish, *Strongylura marina,* the garfish, *Ablennes hians,* also called flat needlefish, and a number of other needlefishes and halfbeaks.

The true freshwater gars of North America include several species of the genus *Lepisosteus.* They are all more or less well known, but perhaps the most familiar is the longnosed gar, *Lepisosteus osseus.*

The shortnosed gar, *Lepisosteus platostomus,* is another well-known gar. Its snout is much shorter and wider than that of the longnosed gar. The alligator gar, *Lepisosteus spatula,* is the giant of the genus. A specimen approaching 10 feet in length and over 300 pounds in weight is on record.

Longnosed Gar
Other Common Names—Northern long-nosed gar, billy gar, bill fish, bony gar, common gar pike, Ohio gar
Scientific Name—*Lepisosteus osseus*
Family—Lepisosteidae (gars)
Order—Semionotiformes
Size—Length, about three feet

Range—In the north it lives in streams from the Minneapolis area to the Great Lakes drainage and east to Vermont, south to Alabama and Mexico

The longnose gar's most outstanding physical characteristic is its snout, which extends into a long, thin beak. The length of this beak is several times the

Long-nosed gar

length of the fish's head. Both jaws are armed with long, sharp teeth. The fish has one dorsal fin; it is set well back near the tail and has about eight rays.

The longnosed gar's back may be brown, yellow, or olive. Its lower sides and belly are yellowish to white. Most specimens have large round, black spots on their dorsal, anal, and tail fins.

The longnosed gar feeds chiefly on other fishes. Like the other gars in its genus, it is not considered good eating or a good game fish. —M.R.

GASTROPOD

Unlike the bivalves, the gastropods, which form the second largest class of the order Mollusca, have only one shell, a univalve, that is usually in the form of a spiral. The gastropods, often called sea snails, include such animals as the limpets, top shells, conch shells, cowries, whelks, abalones, and periwinkles. Fossil gastropods are known as far back as the Cambrian Period (*See Geological Time*).

Primarily a saltwater group, many gastropods live in fresh water and on land, moving about on a muscular foot. The gastropods have distinct heads with eyes, a mouth usually at the end of a proboscis, and one or two pairs of sensory tentacles, or feelers. In all of the various species, the spiral shells in which their bodies are encased have caused a modification of their internal organs. The twisted body structures can be seen even in the embryo—before the shell has formed. A few gastropods have no shell at all—for example, slugs. However, most

Periwinkles cling to a wave-washed rock on the coast of Maine

Close-up of common periwinkle

of them live within shells varying in size from nearly microscopic horn shells to large whelks and abalones nearly a foot long. The shells are closed with a tough plate called the operculum. (*See Bivalve and also Mollusk*) —G.A.B.

Closed gentian

GENTIAN
Closed Gentian
Other Common Names—Blue gentian, barrel gentian, bottle gentian
Scientific Name—*Gentiana andrewsii*
Family—Gentianaceae (gentian family)
Range—Georgia to Arkansas, north to eastern Massachusetts, Vermont, southwestern Quebec, southern Ontario, Manitoba, and Saskatchewan
Habitat—Meadows, damp prairies, low thickets
Time of Blooming—August through October

The deep blue, bottle-shaped flowers that remain almost closed throughout their blooming period present an entrance problem to most insects except the bumblebee. It can force its way inside, where it is sometimes trapped. Sometimes bumblebees use the flower as a place for night retreat.

The plant is a perennial with simple, opposite leaves. The stem is one to two feet high, upright, and smooth. The flowers are mostly clustered at the top of the stem and rise directly from the axils of the leaves. They are occasionally pink or white. This is the most common gentian of the eastern United States; the soapwort gentian, *Gentiana saponaria*, is more common in the central states. The fringed gentian is more famed for its beauty but is much more rare.

Some species of gentian are found in all states, with the exception of those in the south central section. Many small species grow in the alpine meadows, both here and abroad.

In the United States gentians are protected by law in many states.

GEODUCK
Other Common Names—Goeduck
Scientific Name—*Panope generosa*
Family—Saxicavidae (rock-boring clams)
Order—Teleodesmacea
Size—Length, unstretched, 8 to 10 inches
Range—Northwest Pacific Coast of North America, particularly in Puget Sound region of Washington, and in quiet waters down to southern California

The geoduck—pronounced as though spelled *gooeyduck*—is the largest of the burrowing clams. One weighing about 16 pounds has been recorded.

Geoducks live in burrows about three feet below the surface of sand flats at the line of extreme high tide. They keep their two long neck tubes, or siphons at the surface. They feed on tiny marine plants and animals that they suck in through one siphon; wastes and water are pumped out through the other. When disturbed, the geoducks retract their siphons, although these are too big to be completely withdrawn into the shell.

The flesh is red-orange and is edible. Never very common, geoducks have become rarer through overharvesting and are now protected by a closed season and a bag limit.   —G.B.S.

GEOLOGICAL TIME

One of the supreme achievements of modern scientific thought is the concept of geological time, a system of dating the fossil record, land formations, and the age of the earth. Although there had been speculations on many phases of the subject down through the ages, it has only been within the past two hundred years that reliance has been placed on evidence from the earth itself.

Prior to the development of geological knowledge, opinion in the western world favored the belief that the earth was created in six days, as outlined in the Book of Genesis. The date of the event was in dispute, but one 17th-Century scholar, Bishop Ussher, placed it at 4004 B.C. Natural features of the earth that were later to be considered as evidence for a new system of dating were ignored. The layering, or stratification, of rocks had then no known significance, and fossils were either chance formations, creations of the devil, or remains of a former world of life with no connections with currently existing creatures.

It was against this background of ignorance and misinterpretation that the development of scientific geology occurred. The first great forward step came in 1795 with James Hutton's *Theory of the Earth,* in which he wrote that the geological processes that have formed the earth's contours are still continuing and can be observed. He taught that the addition of a few inches of volcanic ash at the mouth of a crater was the same thing on a smaller scale as the creation of ranges of igneous rock; that the deposition of a thin layer of sediment by a flooding stream was the identical process by which vast layers of sedimentary rock have been laid down; and that the gradual rise of landmasses has led to the formation of mountains, plateaus, and even continents.

In 1830 this doctrine was refined by Charles Lyell in his *The Principles of Geology,* which also offered additional evidence. From these beginnings, and with the contributions of generations of geologists, the discipline has acquired a broader scope and firmer foundations.

One of the pillars of the new system was that older rocks underlie younger ones, and that fossils are older as one digs more deeply. Occasionally a pronounced similarity between fossils of different strata was evident, and in some cases this indicated a relationship—for example, that the older form was the ancestor of the younger. Over the years a nearly complete series of fossils from successive strata has been found to illustrate the evolution of many plants as well as of the horse, the elephant, and the rhinoceros, to name a few of the larger animals.

Although modern techniques of calculating time have changed the estimated dates, they confirm the major premises of geological dating. One of the more advanced techniques relies on radioactive elements that occur naturally on earth. When atoms of these elements decay, new elements are formed. If the rate of decay of a given radioactive element in a rock or fossil sample is known, the age of the sample can be computed by comparing the proportion of new and old elements. Radioactive forms of uranium and carbon are two of the more common elements used in determining the ages of rocks and organic matter.

These and other discoveries underlie the science of geology, at least the portion of it that deals with time. All of them conform to the requirements of scientific procedure in that they are completely objective, that all evidence is from the natural world, and that the evidence or the experiments can be examined by anyone for other possible interpretations.

The age of the earth is currently estimated to be between three and ten billion years. Life on the earth is thought to be a comparatively recent development in relation to the age of the universe: The oldest fossils now known are those of primitive plants—algae and fungi —and are about three and a half to four billion years old. The oldest animal fossils, dating back to about two and a half billion years, are those of annelid worms and jellyfish. These, however, are far more complex than many living protozoa, so it is assumed that animal life occurred long before this. At any rate, animal fossils are not common in rocks formed before the Cambrian Period, óne of the seven major divisions of the Paleozoic Era.

The Cambrian Period had its beginning about 600 million years ago and lasted for about 100 million years. The climate was apparently warm, and many forms of life flourished in the seas although the land was barren. Algae, fungi, bacteria, protozoa, sponges, corals, jellyfishes, and mollusks were common, and some were remarkably like present forms. Trilobites, now extinct, appear to have been the dominant creatures.

The Ordovician Period began about 500 million years ago and lasted perhaps 75 million years. The creatures that had survived from the Cambrian Period continued to develop in complexity. Mollusks expanded, both in numbers of species and in size, some kinds growing to 13 feet long. The earliest known remains of the first vertebrate, or animal with a backbone, come from Ordovician strata. It was probably in this period that the first land plants developed from those of the shallows, although the first definite land plant fossils are found in Silurian deposits.

The Silurian Period started 425 million years ago, and lasted some 20 million years. Fishes, crinoids, trilobites, and scorpionlike eurypterids lived among the corals, starfishes, and mollusks, while primitive plants spread óver the land.

The Devonian Period, beginning 405 million years ago and continuing for 60 million years, was the age in which the fishes achieved a tremendous variety (*See under Fish*). Many were encased in bony armor, a trait that was to die out. Sharks were common in Devonian seas. The first amphibians developed from some of the lobe-finned fishes making their way ashore to swampy forests of scale trees, ferns, horsetails, and mosses, where insects and spiders had already become established.

The next two periods—the Mississippian and Pennsylvanian—are often combined as one, the Carboniferous Period. This name refers to the fact that major deposits of coal were formed at this time (*See under Coal*). The coal deposits developed from the great forests of such vegetation as conifers, scale trees, seed ferns, and huge horsetails that flourished in the temperate climate of the time.

The Mississippian Period, beginning 345 million years ago and lasting 45 million years, saw the increasing development of fishes and a waning of the trilobites. On land, amphibians were becoming more diversified. The Pennsylvanian Period, 310 million to 280 million years ago, was a time in which the first reptiles developed from some ancestral amphibian stock (*See under Amphibian, and Reptile*).

In the Permian Period, 280 million to 230 million years ago, trilobites died out, possibly because they were unable to compete with the increasingly more numerous fishes or perhaps because they were eaten by marine reptiles. Among the land reptiles were flesh-eating forms ancestral to the mammals. At the end of the Permian Period a number of worldwide changes occurred, probably connected with the uplifting of continental landmasses and the disappearance of some of the wide, shallow inland seas. Some earlier life forms, including many marine animals and land plants, became extinct. Several deserts appeared, and a large part of the southern hemisphere was glaciated.

The Mesozoic Era, meaning *middle life*, contains the Triassic, Jurassic, and Cretaceous periods. It was the Age of Reptiles, but also a time that saw the appearance and diversification of the mammals and the flowering plants.

The Triassic Period, from 230 million

ERAS	DURATION OF PERIODS	PERIODS			DOMINANT ANIMAL LIFE
CENOZOIC 63 MILLION YEARS DURATION	1	Quaternary		Recent Pleistocene	Man
	63	Tertiary	EPOCHS	Pliocene Miocene Oligocene Eocene Paleocene	Mammals
MESOZOIC 167 MILLION YEARS DURATION	135	Cretaceous			
	181	Jurassic			
	230	Triassic			Dinosaurs
PALEOZOIC 370 MILLION YEARS DURATION	280	Permian			Primitive Reptiles
	310	Pennsylvanian			
	345	Mississippian			
	405	Devonian			Amphibians
	425	Silurian			Fishes
	500	Ordovician			Invertebrates
	600	Cambrian			
PROTEROZOIC **ARCHAEOZOIC**	Figures in millions of years	2,500 + MILLION YEARS DURATION			BEGINNINGS OF LIFE

to 181 million years ago, was one of great diversification of the reptiles, while cycads and conifers spread over the highlands. Marine reptiles became larger, some exceeding 20 feet in length.

During the Jurassic Period, which lasted from 181 to 135 million years ago, the dinosaurs became dominant; no other land animal has ever equaled the bulk of these monsters, some of which weighed 50 tons. More important for later ages were the appearance of the first mammals, ratlike in size and shape, and the first birds (*See under Bird and Mammal*).

In the Cretaceous Period, from 135 million years ago to 63 million years ago, the first of the flowering plants appeared, including oaks, magnolias, maples, and laurels. Huge reptiles were still the dominant animals, but forms similar to the opossum and to the shrews were increasingly common. At the end of the Cretaceous Period the dinosaurs, the flying reptiles, the huge marine reptiles, and many forms of invertebrates became extinct, probably because of widespread climate and geological changes.

The Cenozoic Era, meaning *recent life*, contains six epochs that divide the past 63 million years. It is often called the Age of Mammals, for these warm-blooded creatures superseded the reptiles of the Mesozoic Era, as the flowering plants had superseded the cycads and horsetails of the earlier time.

The Paleocene, the Eocene, and the Oligocene epochs are collectively called the Lower Tertiary Period. The small rodentlike animals that had survived the Cretaceous Period diversified into a wide range of types, including two new groups, the hooved mammals (*see under Deer: Deer Other Hoofed Animals*) and the carnivores (*See under Carnivore*). The shrewlike animals of the Cretaceous Period had now developed into the early primates. Huge rhinoceroses and many large cud-chewing mammals appeared, most of them to become extinct later. The Miocene and the Pliocene epochs,

from 25 to 1 million years ago, saw the evolution of many grazing animals, probably because of continental uplifts that resulted in drier climates and the spread of the grasses that form their diet. Camels, elephants, and horses were widespread; saber-toothed stabbing cats stalked smaller plantfeeders; and creatures resembling modern apes lived in Europe and Africa.

The Quaternary Period includes two epochs—the Pleistocene and the Recent —in which we live.

The Pleistocene can be characterized as the Ice Age, which included four glacial advances that buried much of northern and mountainous North America, Eurasia, and the mountains of the southern hemisphere. Many of the animals of the Upper Tertiary Period did not survive the cold periods; others, such as the members of the elephant family we call mammoths, became covered with thick, woolly hair. During the warmer interglacial times, giant sloths and herds of camels and pigs roamed North America, but these later died out. The most significant development of the Pleistocene Epoch, or the time just prior to it, was the emergence of man.   —G.B.S.

GEOLOGY (*See under Rock Formation*)

GEORGIA (*See under Okefinofee Swamp*)

GERANIUM
Wild Geranium
Other Common Names—Rockweed, sailor's-knot, cranesbill, spotted cranesbill, alumroot
Scientific Name—*Geranium maculatum*
Family—Geraniaceae (geraniums)
Range—Central Maine to Manitoba, southern New England, Long Island, Georgia, Tennessee, Missouri, and Kansas
Habitat—Woods, thickets, and meadows
Time of Blooming—Late April through June

Wild geranium

The wild geranium with its rose-purple, or lavender, flower is a distant relative of the household geranium which is usually derived from a wild geranium of Mexico. The wild *Geranium maculatum* of the woodlands and hedgerows of the eastern half of the United States is more delicate in color and texture than the sturdy cultivated geranium of gardens and flowerpots. Of the nearly 200 species of geranium, more than 60 grow in North America.

The flowers of the geranium family have parts which come in fives or multiples of five. The wild geranium has 5 sepals, 5 petals, 10 stamens in a double circle of 5 each, and a 5-lobed ovary. The flower is from 1 to 1½ inches across. The leaves are five-parted and deeply cut on the margins. Hairs on the stem, leaves, and sepals protect the bloom from those insects, such as ants and beetles, that would not bring about fertilization. Even the flower petals have a tuft of hair at the inner base to prevent rain and dew from trickling into the flower and diluting the sweet nectar, thereby saving it intact for the bees, butterflies, and beelike flies so necessary for cross-pollination and the survival of the species.

To further insure cross-pollination and prevent self-pollination, the anthers of the wild geraniums, which are sometimes a delicate peacock-blue, ripen first, and after they have shed their pollen, fall off before the stigmas of the pistil are ripe for receiving pollen. In this manner the resulting seed will contain characteristics of two parent plants, rather than one. This never ending stream of slight variation insures better opportunity for adaptation and survival.

The fruit of the various wild geraniums is a long pod that looks like a crane's or heron's beak—hence the name also of cranebill, the basis for the name, geranium, which comes from the Greek word for *crane. Maculatum* is derived from a word referring to the brown or white splotches appearing on the older leaves.

The pod of the wild geranium, when ripe, performs one of the more amazing feats of seed dispersal. The right amount of dryness causes it to split into its five segments, each having a seed at its base, and to curl up with a suddenness and force that send the seeds flying some distance from the plant.

The seeds of the wild geranium are eaten by some birds and rodents, including the mourning dove, the bobwhite quail, and chipmunks. Some mammals, including the white-tailed deer in North Carolina, browse upon the plant to a small extent.

The plant of the wild geranium lives for several years and has an enlarged rootstock for food storage. —B.D.

The venom of Gila monsters is fatal to small animals

GILA MONSTER

Other Common Names — Beaded lizard
Scientific Name — *Heloderma suspectum*
(in Mexico, a black-headed species, *Heloderma horridum*)
Family — Helodermatidae (Gila monsters)
Order — Squamata
Size — Length, up to two feet
Range — Arid desert areas of Arizona and New Mexico, south into western Mexico

The Gila monster is the only poisonous lizard in the United States. The poison, formed in modified salivary glands, is not injected but runs down grooves in the lower teeth and is worked into the wound by the action of the jaws. Frequently the Gila monster turns over in order to more effectively inflict the poison into its prey. The venom is fatal to small animals. Although usually a slow moving animal, the Gila monster can bite quickly with a snap of the head. There are few cases on record of Gila monsters biting humans.

Owing to the secretive habits of Gila monsters in the southwestern United States and their failure to breed in captivity, our knowledge of their life history is fragmentary. Courtship probably takes place at night. In Arizona, pairs mating have been observed in the late hours of twilight, usually during the latter part of July. The eggs are probably laid a few days later in the month or early in August. This is ordinarily near the peak of the summer rainy season, when ample heat and moisture are available for the incubation of the eggs.

Normally from four to seven eggs are laid. Reliable information is lacking, but probably a cavity is scooped out of the sand by the female, who carefully covers the nest after laying her eggs. It is also probable that the female digs her nest in a moist place, but one where the developing eggs will not be submerged by the flash floods that characterize the regions inhabited by the Gila monster. Obscure sensory cues seemingly lead most reptiles to nesting sites that are nearly ideal for the incubation of their eggs, but exactly how such sites are chosen remains a mystery.

The relatively enormous eggs of the Gila monster, roughly 2¾ inches long, and 1½ inches in diameter, almost certainly require more than a month to incubate. Contrary to an early account, there is no sign of a developing embryo in the white, leathery-shelled eggs laid by captives. The incubation of the eggs of many reptiles in the United States requires from two to three months, and it is probable that young Gila monsters do not emerge from the nest until September or October. Hatchlings are comparatively large — nearly seven inches long, if we include the 1¼ inches comprising the tail.

Whether they feed prior to going underground for the winter is problematical, but by the end of the following summer they appear to be approaching sexual maturity, with the body length roughly doubled in size. They enter their third season, ready to breed, when approximately 15 or 16 inches long, from snout to tail tip, after which they grow very slowly. A Gila monster that was 19 inches long when captured gained less than 3 inches in length during a 10-year period in captivity.   —C.M.B.

Scarlet gilia

GILIA
Scarlet Gilia
Other Common Names — Skyrocket
Scientific Name — *Gilia aggregata*
Family — Polemoniaceae (polemonium family)
Range — North coast ranges, Sierra Nevada and Panamint Mountains, California north to British Columbia, east to Rocky Mountains
Habitat — Open woods, Transition Zone
Time of Blooming — June to September

We do not see scarlet wild flowers very often. The one in the picture lives in high mountains and has a tall main stem that grows up through underbrush. Each flower is on a short stem. The pointed petals stand straight out from the top of a tube, making the flower look very wide awake. These flowers are like a shower of red stars, giving the plant one of its common names of skyrocket. Our phlox of the garden belong to this family.

GINKGO
Other Common Names — Maidenhair tree
Scientific Name — *Ginkgo biloba*
Family — Ginkgoaceae (ginkgo family)
Range — Native to eastern China but no longer growing wild. Introduced in Japan, Europe, and the United States
Habitat — Grown as a shade or ornamental tree in moist, temperate climates
Leaves — Two to four inches across, fan-shaped, often two-lobed with parallel veins, long slender stems. Clusters of three to five leaves arising from spurs
Bark — Gray, irregularly fissured or furrowed
Flowers — Staminate flowers; catkinlike, on slender axis. Pistillate flowers: long stalked with two ovules
Fruit — Drupelike with a fleshy, ill-smelling, bony inner coat surrounding a large kernel

The ginkgo (a Chinese word meaning *silver fruit*) is the only remaining species of a large family of plants that flourished during the Mesozoic Era, some 135 to 63 millon years ago. Fossil ginkgos are known from nearly all regions of the earth where geological formations of Mesozoic age are found. Like the members of the yew family (Taxaceae), the pine family (Pinaceae), and a few others, the ginkgo is a gymnosperm — a plant that produces seeds that are not enclosed in ovaries.

Originally the ginkgo was probably found growing wild throughout most of eastern China; however, within historical times it has been known only from Chin-

The gingko has unique fan-shaped leaves

cause of the disagreeable odor of the ripe fruits that resemble cherries. The large kernels of these fruits are sweet and edible.

The most unusual feature of the ginkgo is the curious fan-shaped, leathery leaves that are usually notched in the center. These leaves grow in clusters of three to five from little spurs, or short shoots, that project from the branches very much like the tamarack or larch. In autumn the leaves turn bright yellow and are shed. Ginkgos may attain heights up to 140 feet. They are sparsely branched and have spire-shaped crowns. —G.A.B.

GLACIER BAY NATIONAL MONUMENT

Location—Southern Alaska
Size—3,590 square miles
Mammals—Seals, porpoises, whales, wolves, wolverines, coyotes, foxes, deer, beavers, pine martens, black bears, brown bears, grizzly bears, mountain goats
Birdlife—Bald eagles, loons, great blue herons, many geese, ducks, puffins, guillemots, and murrelets
Plants—Spruces, firs, hemlocks, pines, cottonwoods

The Fairweather Mountains, with one ice-capped peak topping 15,320 feet, tower over Icy Strait and the north Pacific. The jagged mountains are scored by bays and inlets, with many rocky islands. Much of the park is above the timberline, and dense forests occur only at low elevations.

The number of glaciers within the park has not been determined, but they are quite common. The most spectacular is Muir Glacier, on Muir Bay. The ice cliff at the glacier's seaward edge is over 250 feet high. Huge fragments of the glacier fall into the water to become icebergs.

Accommodations—In Juneau, Alaska, 50 miles away
Headquarters—Region Four, National Park Service, San Francisco, California

ese temples where it has long been cultivated by monks. The Japanese began to cultivate this interesting living fossil about 1720, and it was introduced into the United States about 1784, where it is grown successfully in the moist temperate regions of the eastern United States and along the Pacific Coast. It is often planted in parks and along city streets and is remarkably tolerant to smoke, wind, dust, ice, and insect pests. Female trees are seldom cultivated be-

Ice-sculptured peaks and glaciers dominate the landscape at Glacier Bay National Monument

Jackson glacier at Glacier National Park in Montana

GLACIER NATIONAL PARK
Location—Northwestern Montana
Size—1,583 square miles
Mammals—Mountain goats, moose, elk, whitetail deer, mule deer, bighorn sheep, cougars, beavers, marmots, pikas, black bears, grizzly bears, snowshoe hares
Birdlife—Golden eagles, bald eagles, loons, grouse, ducks, ptarmigans, jays, crossbills, dippers
Plants—Lodgepole, whitebark, and limber pines; firs, spruces, hemlocks, red cedars, cottonwoods, bear grasses, glacier lilies, columbines

The Continental Divide passes through Glacier National Park; the highest peak within the park boundaries is Mount Cleveland, 10,448 feet above sea level.

Millions of years ago, this region was a shallow sea, with layered deposits of shale and limestone. A buckling of the earth's surface forced the landmasses upward; glacial activity has sculptured them into jagged peaks and ranges. The colors of the sea bottom, preserved in the rock, now gleam from canyon walls, in red, yellows, greens, purples, and grays.

More than 50 small glaciers are within the park, some of them easily accessible. Other features are St. Mary Lake, one of the 200 glacial lakes, and the high peaks capped with snow well into July.

Waterton Lakes National Park, in Canada, lies to the north. The two parks are often called the Waterton-Glacier International Peace Park.

Accommodations—Three hotels within the park, three chalets, public campgrounds
Headquarters—West Glacier, Montana

GLAZE (*See under Frost*)

GNATCATCHER
Blue-gray Gnatcatcher
Other Common Names—Sylvan flycatcher, little bluish-gray wren
Scientific Name—*Polioptila caerulea*
Family—Sylviidae (Old World warblers,

Blue-gray gnatcatcher (male, above; female, below)

gnatcatchers, and kinglets)
Order—Passeriformes
Size—Length, 4½ inches
Range—California, central Nevada, southern Utah and Colorado, eastern Nebraska, Minnesota, southern Wisconsin, Michigan, Ontario, and Ohio, New York, and northern New Jersey south through Mexico to Guatemala, the Gulf Coast, and the Bahamas

This slender, graceful little bird with its absurdly long tail, often seems a miniature reproduction of the mockingbird. The blue-gray gnatcatcher is active and restless, constantly flitting and darting about among the upper foliage of the trees, its movements accompanied by high-pitched, nasal notes. The blue-gray gnatcatcher's expertness as a catcher of small insects is matched by its skill in handling its long tail, which in breezy weather is often blown awry. The favorite haunt of this bird is rather open woodland, but it is also found in orchards and in the timber bordering streams and roadsides. As an acrobat the blue-gray gnatcatcher takes high rank and goes through remarkable gyrations as it darts about after small prey. The grotesque movements are all the more accentuated by the long tail, which gracefully opens and closes.

The blue-gray gnatcatcher is not at all shy, and particularly during the nest-building time pays little attention to human observers. The nest is a model of artistry, made of plant fibers, strips of bark, and various other fine materials and is covered over with lichens. The female lays four to five bluish-white eggs, thickly speckled with various shades of brown.

GOAT
Mountain Goat
Other Common Names—Rocky Mountain goat, goat antelope
Scientific Name—*Oreamnos americanus*
Family—Bovidae (cattle, sheep, and goats)
Order—Artiodactyla
Size—Male: body length, 5 to 5¾ feet; height at shoulder, 3 to 3½ feet; weight, 125 to 300 pounds. Female: slightly smaller
Range—Mountains of northwestern North America, from southeastern Alaska and the Yukon south to southwestern Alberta, northern Idaho, and the mountains of Montana and Washington; introduced elsewhere

There is probably no large mammal in North America with more unique features than the mountain goat. Wild mountain goats, living as they do above timberline in remote and inaccessible regions of the Rocky Mountains, are seldom seen except by a few hardy naturalists.

They pick their way carefully across treacherous slides of loose rock and

The mountain goat, Oreamnos americanus (above), is sometimes confused with the bighorn, or mountain sheep, Ovis canadensis (below), and the white bighorn, or Dall's sheep, Ovis dalli. The mountain goat has a beard under its chin, and its slender, spiky horns project upward and slightly back; the bighorn has no beard, and the broadbased, massive horns sweep abruptly outward, and, in large specimens, curl forward.

sheer cliffs, the cup-shaped soles of their sharp hooves gripping the rock and preventing a slip. If the trail fades away to nothing they show no alarm, but cautiously and deliberately retrace their steps. The most inaccessible crags are their year-round home, from which they rarely descend even in winter gales. When the alpine meadows where they feed in summer are buried beneath the snow, they eke out a living on the sparse, exposed vegetation of windswept ridges.

Mountain goats have a hairy covering that is well suited to protect them from the icy winds with which they have to contend. Fine wool, three to four inches thick, snugly encloses their bodies, and coarse, longer hairs form a shaggy overcoat. The mountain goat is the only native North American mammal that produces wool, and unlike most species, the mountain goat's coat remains white throughout the year. Goats shed their wool from time to time, and in some areas a large amount may be gathered within a short period. The potential value of this wool was recognized by the Indians many years ago. They gathered it, dyed it various colors, and wove it into blankets and robes. The famous Chilkat blankets and robes are perhaps the best known of these.

Mountain goats are heavily built animals with short, stumpy legs. Both sexes have beards and horns, and the horns, being black, stand out in striking contrast to the white coat. Males are somewhat larger than the females, and they are reported, in some areas, to average nearly 200 pounds. There is, however, considerable individual variation. One male of 276 pounds is on record, and one enormous specimen, killed in Alaska in 1913, is reported to have weighed 502 pounds.

This animal is certainly goatlike in appearance and habits, but technically it is not a goat at all. It differs from true goats in several important respects. The horns are short and remain straight rather than growing into spirals. Behind each horn there is an oil gland that, so far as is known, does not occur in this position in any other animal. The creature is actually a type of antelope and is more closely related to the famed chamois of the Alps than to members of the goat tribe. The various common names, all including the word goat, are so well accepted, however, that they are not likely to be changed.

There is still much to be learned about the habits of mountain goats, but thanks to hunters and naturalists as well as to observations of captive animals, considerable information has accumulated through the years. Mating occurs once each year and the kids are born between April and June. Single births are the rule, but occasionally twins are born. The youngsters are precocious and may jump and frolic within an hour or so after birth.

For several days after the kid is born, it and the mother remain isolated from others of their kind. The youngster feeds on milk from the mammary glands of the female, just as other mammals do. As the kid develops it starts nibbling at the sparse vegetation that grows at high altitudes. Lichens, mosses, mountain sorrel, and other hardy plants allow the mountain goats to live where many other herbivorous animals would starve. During the spring and summer the females with their kids congregate in groups as they graze on the mountain slopes.

The males are often solitary and they sometimes have a tendency to stand at the edge of a precipice while calmly gazing at the landscape. They are not normally aggressive, but if cornered they will not hesitate to attack anything from a human being to a grizzly bear. Also, during the breeding season, which is usually in November, the males do become pugnacious for a short period. During this time they thrash the bushes and rocks with their horns, and sometimes two males will fight for the favor of a female. This battle is normally not to the death, although if one of the contestants suffers a deep wound he may die later of infection.

The enemies of mountain goats include cougars, or mountain lions, bears, wolves, and eagles, in addition to the human beings who hunt them. They are also subject to parasites such as tapeworms and ticks. Goats generally give a good account of themselves in defense of their lives and their daggerlike horns are effective weapons. Their horns are of the hollow type and are never shed by either sex.

Many naturalists believe that snowslides kill more goats than any other single factor, but this cataclysm of nature also operates in the animals' favor, for at times when there are likely to be avalanches and snowslides, human hunters avoid the high mountains where the goats live. Much of the time the goats are on peaks above the snowslides, but the animals are exposed if they descend into the valleys and ravines.

The mountain goat is undoubtedly a better mountaineer than the mountain sheep (*see under Sheep*) or any other species of North American mammal. The regions frequented by the mountain goat are much less accessible to humans than those of the mountain sheep. Some naturalists maintain that goats routinely traverse trails of such difficulty that mountain sheep will not try them unless trying to escape a greater danger. During the winter, goats remain at high altitudes, while the mountain sheep descend to lower levels.

The mountain goat appears to have been less affected by man than any other North American mammal, and its range is essentially the same today as it was many years ago. Even in the future, human beings are not likely to invade the haunts of the goats in large numbers. For this reason there is hope that these bearded, cud-chewing patriarchs of the mountains will be safe from extinction for many years to come.

—O.P.B.

Mountain goat

Godetia

GODETIA

Other Common Names—Giant or Whitney's godetia
Scientific Name—*Godetia Whitneyi*
Family — Onagraceae (evening primrose family
Range — Humboldt and Mendocino Counties California
Habitat—Hills near the coast, upper Sonoran Zone
Time of Blooming—June to July

From April to July and August the godetias add much to the passing show of color. On northern coast hills appears the colorful one illustrated, the plant of stocky habit, petals rather wide spread and somewhat resembling our cultivated petunia; from Tuolomne and Tulare Counties south along the mountain front to Riverside County we find *Godetia dudleyana*, stems up to 2½ feet high, petals much smaller and of more cuplike habit, pink with crimson dotted center; *Godetia bottae*, up to 3 feet high, pink or light crimson, follows the hill and chaparral slopes of the San Gabriel and Santa Monica Mountains, thence north along the coast (May and June); a variety of the latter, var. *cylindrica*, calyx indigo purple, petals lilac purple, is in central California; *Godetia amoena*, petals lilac crimson, darker central blotch, northern coast; *Godetia quadrivulnera*, lilac, very common throughout California on west side of mountain ranges. In many species the calyx lobes have a curious habit of uniting and turning away from the flower. The petals close at night.

GODWIT
Marbled Godwit

Other Common Names—Brant bird, marlin, red curlew, badger bird
Scientific Name—*Limosa fedoa*
Family—Scolopacidae (woodcock, snipe, and sandpipers)
Order—Charadriiformes
Size—Length, 18 inches
Range—Central Alberta, southern Saskatchewan, Manitoba, south to central Montana and North Dakota, northeastern South Dakota, and western Minnesota. Winters in central California, western Nevada, southeastern Texas, the Gulf Coast, south to Central America, Peru, and Chile

A birdwatcher is lucky to see more than a few marbled godwits in a season along the Atlantic Coast, but on the Pacific Coast, particularly in California, flocks of hundreds are commonplace. As large as a small duck, the marbled godwit can be identified by its barred, brown color and its very long, straight or slightly upturned bill. Marbled godwits breed inland on the northern prairies and migrate to the coast when nesting is over. The alarm notes of the marbled godwit are given in a loud,

Marbled godwit

shrill series, but they are more rasping than those of the willet—a species with which it commonly associates in winter on tidal mud flats and beaches.

GOLDENROD
California Goldenrod
Other Common Names—Common goldenrod
Scientific Name— *Solidago californica*
Family—Compositae (composite family)
Range — Southwestern Oregon through the Sierra Nevada to San Diego County, and Inyo County
Habitat—Common in dry or moist fields, clearings and forest openings
Time of Blooming—July to October

This cheerful goldenrod is commonly found in western mountain valleys and meadows. The stem is from four to five feet high, small yellow flowers making up the pointed head that is sometimes a foot long. The tiny stamens in the center of each flower are very long, giving the flower an airy look. One goldenrod grows along the coast on sandy hills and another grows at an elevation of 9,000 feet. In early days the plant was cut into small pieces and boiled. This liquid was then used as a healing wash for cuts.

Goldenrods in bloom are associated with crisp, fall days, some flowering as late as November and even December. However, a few show their gold as early as July. They belong to the largest family of flowering plants, the Compositae, whose small five-petaled florets are closely grouped into a head which has the appearance of a single flower.

About 125 species of goldenrod (*Solidago*) occur in America, and only a few species in the rest of the world. For perfect identification, the structure of the small florets should be studied, but fairly accurate determinations may be made by observation of the more obvious leaf and stem characters, the arrangement of flowerheads, and the plant's habitat.

Several gamebirds eat its leaves—especially the prairie chicken. Some songbirds eat the seeds. Beavers, porcupines, and rabbits eat the foliage and stems, and the white-tailed deer browses upon the plants. The wood rat and meadow and pine mice eat the seed heads and foliage.

The goldenrods are perennial plants that will grow in rather sterile soil and for that reason become important in areas where erosion has started, as they will be among the first plants to grow there.

Goldenrod in Open Places
Canada goldenrod, *Solidago canadensis*. The Canada goldenrod is one of the most showy of those with yellow flowers.

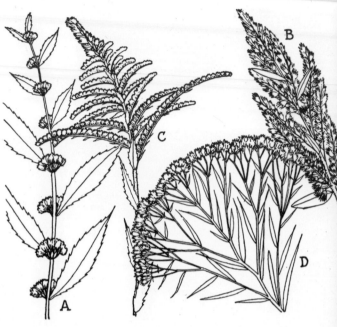

TYPES OF FLOWER CLUSTERS IN THE GOLDENRODS (*All much reduced*)

A. *Solidago caesia*;   B. *Solidago speciosa*;   C. *Solidago rugosa*;   D. *Solidago graminifolia*.

A. Heads chiefly in clusters or short racemes in the axils of ordinary foliage leaves, or occasionally the upper crowded into a leafy cluster terminating the stem.

B. Heads chiefly in erect, compact, terminal clusters, the individual racemes or branches of the cluster either short and arranged along a more or less elongated central axis, or elongated and ascending, scarcely recurved, forming a narrow panicle, never in one-sided clusters.

C. Heads produced on one side only of a more or less elongated, spreading, usually recurved branch, all the branches together forming a terminal widened panicle.

D. Heads crowded at or near the ends of the branches at about the same distance from the base of the panicle, forming a rounded or flat-topped inflorescence.

It produces a flower head shaped like an elm tree (*see under Elm*) and is just as common in the United States as in Canada. Its alternate, slender, prominently three-veined, smooth leaves gradually diminish in size as they reach the top of the stem that may be five feet tall.

Hairy goldenrod, *Solidago rugosa*. A tall, rough, stout plant whose leaves are prominently net-veined. Flower heads are in terminal panicles.

Tall goldenrod, *Solidago altissima*. A tall, stout, hairy plant with narrow leaves having three veins strongly marked and approximately parallel, the upper one sessile. Flower heads in spreading panicles. Very common in dry places.

Flat-topped goldenrod, *Solidago lanceolata*. A very common plant with long, narrow leaves, sometimes with black spots. Leaves are aromatic when bruised. Flower heads in flat or umbrellalike clusters.

Early goldenrod, *Solidago juncea*. Very common everywhere in open fields and roadsides from the end of July until late in the fall. Its stem is often purple. Leaves are sharply toothed, sessile on the stem, and the lower ones are large with long, winged petioles. Flower heads in panicles.

Gray goldenrod, *Solidago nemoralis*. This is a small plant with beautiful flowers on the upper branches of the stem, seemingly covered with dust, but really with minute, fine hairs. The upper leaves are small; the lower leaves are large, spatulate, with winged petioles. Very common in dry, open fields.

Showy goldenrod, *Solidago speciosa*. A very graceful, tall, stout plant with thick ovate leaves, the upper ones sessile, the lower ones large with winged petioles. Branches erect, parallel to the main stem. Common in some sandy places.

Sweet-scented goldenrod, *Solidago odora*. Often grows in sandy places. This is a tall, slender plant with stemless, linear, lanceolate leaves which when crushed are anise-scented. Flower heads grow in panicles.

Goldenrods in Wet Places

Spreading goldenrod, *Solidago patula*. A very tall, stout plant, with an angled stem. The leaves are rough above; the lower ones with winged petioles are very large, spreading over the ground. Flower heads are panicled. Common in swampy woods.

Late goldenrod, *Solidago serotina*. This is another goldenrod rather common in wet places. It is a tall plant with a smooth shiny stem and three-ribbed, sharply toothed leaves. On the whole, it resembles the tall goldenrod, *Solidago altissima*.

Goldenrods in Woods

Wreath goldenrod, *Solidago caesia*. This plant is common in woods. Its smooth, slender stem branches at the top; the leaves are sharply toothed, smooth, lanceolate, bearing clusters of flowers in their axils. The stem is bluish, with a whitish bloom.

Silver rod, *Solidago bicolor*. This goldenrod differs from the rest by its light flowers which are yellow and white. It is a sturdy plant with spatulate root leaves and flowers growing in the axils of small leaves. Common in dry woods.

Cut-leaved goldenrod, *Solidago arguta*. A stout, smooth plant with lower leaves broad, large, sharply toothed, and winged petioles; upper leaves stemless. Flower heads in panicled racemes. Grows in rich woods.

Goldenrods Along the Seashore

Seaside goldenrod, *Solidago sempervirens*. This goldenrod usually grows in salt marshes and on sea beaches. Its stem is stout, the upper leaves are long, narrow, stemless, fleshy; the lower leaves are spatulate. Flower heads are in panicles.

Slender flat-topped goldenrod, *Solidago tenuifolia*. This small plant resembles flat-topped goldenrod, *Solidago lanceolata*, as the flower heads are arranged in a flat-topped cluster, but the leaves are very narrow, one-nerved. Grows in sandy places along the shore.
— M.H.

Recommended Reading

American Wildflowers—Harold Moldenke. Van Nostrand Company, Princeton, New Jersey.
Flora of Northern United States and Canada—Britton and Brown. Charles Scribner's Sons, New York.
Manual of Botany—Asa Gray. American Book Company, New York.

GOLDFINCH
American Goldfinch

Other Common Names — Yellowbird, wild canary
Scientific Name—*Spinus tristis*
Family—Fringillidae (grosbeaks, finches, sparrows, and buntings)
Order—Passeriformes
Size—Length, 5 to 5½ inches
Range—Breeds from southern Canada to South Carolina, Louisiana, Texas, Nevada and California. Winters from Cana-

An American goldfinch feeds its hungry nestlings

da to Mexico, the Gulf Coast, and Florida

The American goldfinch is the state bird of Iowa, New Jersey, and Washington. No other bird sings with greater ecstasy or abandon. The notes tumble over each other in canarylike profusion. No bird seems to enjoy the sociability of the flock more. Perhaps that is why the month of August often rolls around before goldfinches in the East set about to raising their families.

The American goldfinch is a small yellow bird with black wings, cap, and tail. The yellow warbler shares with it the common names, *yellowbird* and *wild canary*. The bright plumage molts to a dull olive at the approach of colder weather; then, male and female look very much alike. The best clue to the American goldfinch's identity when seen at a great distance is the "roller-coaster" flight—up and down the bird goes, each dip punctuated by a sweet twitter sounding like *perchickory* or *just-look-at-me*. With the warm days of advancing spring the yellow returns to the feathers of the male bird—not by a slow blending process, but quite suddenly. Many of the males are all spotted and patched for a few days. Even the females become somewhat brighter.

In the East, August is the usual month for nesting—July at the very earliest. Most other birds except the cedar waxwing among songbirds, have finished nesting by this time and have their young on the wing. Perhaps the reason for this delay is that goldfinch nests are invariably lined with a layer of thistledown, which is not available until the end of summer. On the other hand, the thistledown might happen to be in the nest because it is available to birds that build at such a late date. In the West nesting takes place earlier, usually in May or June, and the bird does not seem to be so dependent on thistledown for its nests.

The nest is built in a horizontal fork 4 to 20 feet from the ground. It is so neatly and compactly built of grasses, fibers, and plant down that it will hold water. If the nest is built in a shade tree, the large protecting overhead leaves shed the rain during storms, but in more unsheltered nests the young are sometimes drowned. Perhaps the goldfinch builds too good a nest. If it were more loosely constructed the water could trickle through.

The five bluish-white eggs are incubated by the female for 11 to 14 days. Although the eggs all hatch, seldom more than three of the young reach the flying stage. The others are either shoved out or smothered at the bottom of the nest. Even so, goldfinches seem to thrive, for they are quite abundant.

The young are fed by regurgitation; that is, the parent bird fills its crop with seeds and then feeds all the young at one time, producing one seed after another like a magician pulling rabbits from a hat. American goldfinches eat the seeds of the family Compositae—seeds of dandelion, burdock, and chickory.

But seeds are not the only food of goldfinches. The adults feed the young on caterpillars, beetles, grasshoppers, and plant lice. At two weeks, the young birds are well feathered. They resemble the mother and, except for their bobbed tails, almost seem as grown up, but their appearance is deceiving. The young still cannot care for themselves. It takes several weeks for them to learn that a seed comes from a plant and not from the parent birds. Very small, young goldfinches have been found in the nest as late as October. This is exceptional as most of them have assumed the somber plumage of winter by that time and have flocked together. The majority of goldfinches winter in the southern half of the United States, but many stay as far north as the Canadian border.

—A.B., Jr.

GOOSE

Geese belong to the great family of waterfowl, the Anatidae, which also includes close relatives, the swans and the ducks. Swans are the largest, ducks the smallest, and the geese are in between. Proportionate neck length follows the same order.

All geese have plump bodies, short legs, webbed feet, and a high-bridged bill that is fringed on the sides of the gape with plates called *lamellae*, strainers to filter food particles from the water. These birds are almost wholly vegetarian, although some will eat marine invertebrates (*See Invertebrate*). Generally they prefer aquatic vegetation, grains, and grasses.

Most species are believed to mate for life, or at least for the life of either partner. They are very solicitous for the young. Varying numbers of family groups join together to form the familiar V-shaped flocks that indicate the changing of the seasons to those who live along the migration flyways. The families stay together on the wintering grounds and make the journey north in the same company.

Most geese breed on the arctic tundra. The Canada goose is the exception; it nests from the arctic regions south into New England and northern California. This species, along with the common brant, the snow goose, the blue goose, and the white-fronted goose, winters on both coasts of North America; the emperor goose, Ross' goose, and the black brant are found only in the West.

Great numbers of geese winter in the tidal marshes and bays of Virginia and North Carolina, Louisiana and Texas, and the Sacramento and San Joaquin Valleys in California. Federal and state wildlife refuges in each of these areas insure that a portion of the vast flocks will survive the hunting pressure and maintain the species.   —G.B.S.

Canada Goose

Other Common Names — Wild goose, cravat goose, Canada brant, honker
Scientific Name — *Branta canadensis*
Family — Anatidae (swans, geese, and ducks)
Order — Anseriformes
Size — Length, 22 to 39½ inches
Range — Breeds chiefly on the mainland of Canada, to the north and to the west of the Gulf of St. Lawrence; less commonly, south to New England, South Dakota, northern Utah, and northern California. Winters from Great Lakes and Nova Scotia south to Florida and Mexico

On a fair March morning a wedge of geese tracing its way north across the skies looks like a squadron of planes in V formation. The flock shifts and wavers, trying to keep in order behind the leader. They are a symbol—a sign of spring. The arrival of the robin, the bluebird, or the meadowlark is not nearly so full of meaning to the winter-weary country folk as the sight of the migrating geese. The farmer, plowing the newly thawed earth, pauses to watch their passage, feeling confident for the first time that the backbone of winter has been broken. The peak of the migration reaches the northern rim of the United States about the first of April. Then the noisy formations can often be heard passing over the cities at night, flock after flock, intent on reaching less civilized landscapes before daybreak.

The Canada goose is a gray-brown bird with a black head and neck. A prominent feature is a heavy white stripe that resembles a chin strap and runs from one side of its head to the other. Once the Canada goose probably nested over large sections of the United States, but with the settlement of the country it gradually moved north. Today, it is truly a Canadian bird, hardy enough to survive even on the barren islands of the Arctic.

Wild geese are very faithful to each other, mates remaining together for many years. The down-lined nest is placed on dry ground, on a high spot in a marsh, on a rock, or on a small island. There the male stands guard over his mate while she broods. Should an enemy come, she flattens her long snaky neck on the ground and he holds his head high and hisses at the intruder. The hisses are only a warning. Should the unwelcome visitor—man, fox, or dog—come too close, he swings into action. A blow from his wings is not soon forgotten. The five to nine buffy-white eggs take nearly a month to hatch. The fuzzy, yellowish youngsters are able to swim as soon as they have dried.

There comes a time in every goose family, usually late in summer, when neither the old nor the young can fly.

Canada goose

The young geese have not developed their wings fully and their parents have molted their long flight feathers. It is a difficult period, but they survive. It is no easy trick to catch a grown goose, even when it is flightless. If hard-pressed it can even dive under water.

A goose feeds by tipping-up so that its head is under water. The depth from which it can pull up water plants depends on the length of its neck. A variety of water plants are eaten. In saltwater marshes eelgrass is a favorite. When eelgrass is not present in the salt bays, the birds may graze in fields, picking the tender shoots of grasses among the stubble. They also like insects, especially grasshoppers.

When the first frosts drive the geese out of the half-frozen bays of the north, the southward disappearing flocks are a sign that winter is close at hand. There seems to be something melancholy in autumn in their voices; an imaginary thought, perhaps, but certainly the joyous ring of the spring flight seems to have disappeared.   —A.B.,Jr.

GOOSEFISH (*See Angler under Fish: Some Common Marine Fishes of the North Atlantic Coast*)

GOPHER

In North America the word *gopher* is often used in a general way to designate any number of medium-sized burrowing rodents — for example, prairie dogs, ground squirrels, or woodchucks. Properly, however, the word should only be applied to a large group of rodents that belong to the family Geomyidae— the pocket gophers.

Five of the eight genera of pocket gophers are confined wholly to Mexico; of the remaining three, only two, *Thomomys* and *Geomys*, are widely represented in the United States and Canada. The third genus, *Cratogeomys*, or yellow-faced pocket gophers, is represented by one species—the Mexican pocket gopher, *Cratogeomys castanops*. These three genera may be distinguished from one another by the grooves on the outer surface of the upper incisor teeth. In the genus *Thomomys* each of the two incisors has one groove that is either faint or altogether lacking; in the genus *Geomys* each incisor has two very distinct grooves; in the genus *Cratogeomys*, there is one distinct groove on each upper incisor.

Most pocket gophers vary in length from about 8 to 13 inches. Their tails are either lacking or very short and are only sparsely covered with hair, if at all.

Like other animals that spend nearly all of their lives underground, the pocket gophers have strong digging claws on stout forelegs, reduced eyes, and small ears. These modifications are readily noticeable in the bony skeleton. In addition, all of the pocket gophers have fur-lined cheek pouches on the sides of their faces that open externally to the front. These pouches resemble pockets, from which the group gets its common name.

Within North America there are more than 250 subspecies of pocket gophers. By far the greatest number of these are assigned to the genus *Thomomys*, which is confined to the western half of the United States and Canada. The genus *Geomys* has representatives in the central and southeastern United States and ranges into Mexico; the genus *Cratogeomys* is limited to southeastern Colorado, eastern New Mexico, western Oklahoma, and Texas down into northern Mexico.

Among the more common species of the genus *Thomomys* are the northern pocket gopher, *Thomomys talpoides;* the southern pocket gopher, *T. umbrinus;* Bailey's pocket gopher, *T. baileyi;* Townsend's pocket gopher, *T. townsendii;* and the mountain pocket gopher; *T. monticola.*

Two common members of the genus *Geomys* are found in the United States. They are the Plains pocket gopher, *Geomys bursarius,* and the southeastern pocket gopher, *G. pinetus.* A few others —for example, the desert pocket gopher, *G. arenarius*—have very restricted ranges, as do the 20 subspecies of the yellow-faced pocket gopher, *Cratogeomys castanops,* that comprise the genus *Cratogeomys.*   —G.A.B.

Mountain Pocket Gopher
Other Common Names—Gopher
Scientific Name—*Thomomys monticola*
Family— Geomyidae (pocket gophers)
Order—Rodentia
Size—Length of body, 5 ½ to 6 inches;

tail, 2 to 3 inches; weight, 2½ to 3 ½ ounces

Range—Mountains of the western coast from Washington border (Columbia River) south through Oregon, and northern and central California

The mountain pocket gopher prefers a dry slope beneath the trees or a high well-drained home in the meadow. The gopher likes to eat roots as well as the foliage of plants; if its home becomes too damp, it will move rather than get its feet wet.

In the duff beneath the red firs and lodgepole pines growing at the edge of a meadow, circular mounds of soft earth often reveal the homes of the mountain pocket gopher. Like other pocket gophers, the mountain pocket gopher resembles a small meadow mouse, but it has a very short tail, a dark brownish-black coat, and deep fur-lined cheek pockets, which it uses for carrying food and nesting materials. Its long, strong incisors are extremely important for digging its burrow, cutting food and nesting material, defending itself from predators, and fighting off other individuals of its species.

From the shadow of the trees, this gopher's mounds may continue out into the higher, well-drained portions of the meadow. Although very little activity appears to be going on judging from evidence above the ground, the subterranean passages below the mounds of the gopher are centers of great industry. Here, except briefly during the mating season, a solitary householder digs its way through the soil, enlarging its burrow, storing food, preparing a nest cavity, and shoveling out excess soil from its newly dug home to make the piles of soft earth that are so evident in the midst of the green grasses and other herbage of the meadow.

The removal of earth from the clogged passages is a tedious as well as dangerous chore for the mountain pocket gopher. After digging its tunnel to the surface of the ground, the gopher returns, scoops up the soft earth in its forearms, rushes up the tunnel, and throws the load forcibly as far as it can beyond the opening. Before the cleaning job is finished, the little rodent may grow hungry. At such times it may venture out from the safety of its hole, pull up a plant, drag it back into the burrow, and eat it. Such activity may attract the attention of a prowling coyote. If the nearsighted eyes of this little rodent are successful in spotting the predator quickly enough, it may escape into the safety of its dark tunnel and outwit the sly coyote. Sometimes too, as it comes to the surface with its arms full of earth, gray foxes, hawks, owls, and even a black bear may notice the movement and catch the gopher before it can withdraw into its burrow.

Fortunately for the gopher, much of its work is done below the ground. Here it gathers tubers, bulbs, and the roots that grow down into its burrow. Sometimes it pulls an entire plant into its sanctuary without showing even so much as a whisker above the surface. If the animal's hunger is satisfied, it cuts the plants into short pieces, which it stuffs into its fur-lined cheek pockets and carries to one of its pantries for storage. These pantries are dug by the gopher as offshoots from the main tunnel of its burrow. In these pantries the gopher stores large quantities of food for use during the winter.

Gophers do not hibernate, even at high altitudes where snow may reach a depth of 15 feet on level ground. However, winter for them is a period of less activity. They spend considerable time resting in their warm nests or running along their subterranean tunnels from one storeroom to the next, feeding on the "groceries" they put away for just such an emergency.

But as the heavy snows thin, the busy gopher may leave its stores to dig for fresh roots under the snow blanket. Just as in summer the burrower must get

Pocket gopher

rid of excess soil by piling it on top of the ground, so in the winter the rodent pushes the remains of its digging out of the hole under the surface of the snow. This excess earth forms hard earth cores which sometimes reach a length of more than 35 feet. By this method the gopher extends its "subways" and is able to meet the needs of its compact little body. When spring comes, the snow melts and the long black ridges of earth are uncovered—evidence of a busy winter spent below the ground by this industrious little worker.

In addition to the subways, pantries, and nest chambers, the gopher equips its home with a "bathroom" which it uses exclusively for its body wastes. Thus the subways are always clean and fresh. Many other animals provide such sanitary facilities when possible. The mountain beaver, *Aplodontia rufa*, has a similar disposal chamber for maintaining sanitation in its underground tunnels. If the burrow accidentally becomes soiled with excrement the mountain beaver picks up the round pellets with its paws, places them in its mouth, and carries them to the disposal chamber. The pocket gopher is a prodigious eater and a strict vegetarian. Consequently, a great deal of undigested roughage is eliminated, so that special rooms set aside to take care of these wastes are essential in order to prevent clogging of the burrow system.

Gophers are hermits. They live alone except during the mating season when the male invades the female's burrow, mates, and then is driven away. When the young are weaned, they are also expelled from their mother's burrow to make their own way in the world beneath the earth. Adult mountain pocket gophers have short tempers and are great fighters, often battling until one is killed.

The pocket gopher is a tiller of the soil —turning it over, mixing it with plant materials, and opening it up so that air and moisture can enter. It burrows deep beneath the surface of the ground; this helps to prevent soil erosion resulting from too rapid runoff, since the rains and melting snows follow the runways deep into the earth. Thus the little burrower is a water conservationist at a depth where the roots of the firs, lodgepoles, and other vegetation may draw up water into their leaves to manufacture food for their own use and that of other living things. The water also evaporates into the air and rises into the atmosphere where it is later returned to the earth as rain or snow. In this way the pocket gopher plays an important part in the community, a role that involves its life with the great firs and pines, the meadow mouse, the trout in the brook, the coyote on the prowl, and all other plants and animals that live in the high altitude forest.   —E.I.

GOSHAWK (*See under Accipiter*)